Hello, I'm Crystal Wright, and I want to welcome you to 30 DAYS AT 100 PERCENT, a program I created to help you and me reclaim the best that we can be by identifying and striving to maintain 100% in all areas of our lives.

30 DAYS AT 100 PERCENT is broken into three phases. The first 30 days is FOCUS, the second 30 days is MOMENTUM, and the final 30 days is ACHIEVEMENT.

The program is designed to help us identify and rid ourselves of the distractions that keep us enslaved to a life half-lived. We can all do better. And we will, 30 days at a time.

Come with me. If you'll choose me as your coach, I will not let you down. I want to walk you through this new journey to reclaim your 100 PERCENT, 30 DAYS AT A TIME.

Crystal Wright

CRYSTAL WRIGHT'S

30 DAYS

100 PERCENT

CHANGING YOUR LIFE 30 DAYS AT A TIME

MOTIVATIONAL MEDIA PRODUCTIONS
LOS ANGELES, CALIFORNIA

CRYSTAL WRIGHT'S
30 DAYS AT 100 PERCENT
Changing Your Life 30 Days at a Time

Copyright © 2009, 2010 by Crystal A. Wright.
30 DAYS AT 100 PERCENT
is a trademark of Tacoma Girl, Inc.

Published by Motivational Media Productions
6709 La Tijera Blvd., Ste 836
Los Angeles, CA 90045
(323) 299-0500
www.30DAYSAT100PERCENT.com

Third Edition

FOREWORD

A decade, that is how long I have known Crystal A. Wright, the girl from Tacoma, Washington, as she so proudly states. She is a woman and friend who continually demonstrates what 'fabulous' is. She is fabulous, no doubt about it, yet there is this underlying quality about her that no matter your background, social status, race, gender, or religion she makes you feel like the most important person in the room when she speaks to you. I have always referred to it as her 'X-Factor.' It is something that comes from within, and is really a gift from God for those who meet her and a continual blessing to those who really know her, and call her friend. I once read that great individuals are identifiable because they are in a state of complete freedom of themselves, that their character defects (and don't we all have some?) do not control them. They live entirely in the now, giving full attention and energy to the present moment. This is the perfect description of Crystal. This described what I have always called her 'X-Factor'.

Only God knew what He was doing some five short months ago when Crystal, Fleacé, and I committed to each other to start reading selected spiritually enriching books and review the chapters together at 7:00AM twice weekly via conference calls. It was during this quest of ours when we all sought to grow closer to God and his individual purpose for us that He revealed to Crystal her purpose through 30 DAYS AT 100 PERCENT.

I am so excited for you to begin your journey using 30 DAYS AT 100 PERCENT. Being open to what God will reveal on this journey is a bold move and I am proud of you. If you lean forward, take action and search within to claim your 100%, God can begin to open up your world in ways you would never have dreamed or imagined. I pray that each of you will allow God to guide you to your 100% so you, too can share your 'X-Factor,' your very own unique 'God Factor' with those lucky people who come in contact with you.

—Kathy Blount

TABLE OF CONTENTS

FOREWORD 05

TABLE OF CONTENTS 06

INTRODUCTION ....**12 - 17**

THE LESSON 12

THE FIRST 30 DAYS 13

WHERE TO BEGIN 13

THE BENEFITS OF BEING 100% 14

WHAT HAPPENED TO MY 100% 15

MAINTAINING 100% 15

HOW 30 DAYS WORKS 16

CIRCLE OF FRIENDS 17

WORKIN' THE PLAN ....**18 - 47**

STEP 1: WHAT TO DO FIRST 18

STEP 2: CONFERENCE CALLS ....18 - 19

STEP 3: TAKE INVENTORY 20

STEP 4: FILL IN THE BLANKS 20

EXAMPLE: CRYSTAL'S AREAS OF OPPORTUNITY - PERSONAL INVENTORY 21

MY AREAS OF OPPORTUNITY: PERSONAL ....22 - 23

MY AREAS OF OPPORTUNITY: PROFESSIONAL ....24 - 25

STEP 5: REVIEW 27

STEP 6: RECORD 27

EXAMPLES: CRYSTAL'S 100% + CRYSTAL'S 100% PAYOFF............28 - 29

MY 100% PERSONAL + MY 100% PAYOFF ....30 - 31

MY 100% PROFESSIONAL + MY 100% PAYOFF ....32 - 33

EVERY DAY AT 100% 34

STEP 7: MASTERING TRIGGERS & CONTROLS ....34 - 35

TRIGGERS & CONTROLS ....36 - 37

STEP 8: PREPARATION 38

CONFERENCE CALL 1 - WEEK 1 39

STEP 9: YOUR STORY 40

STEP 10: WHAT'S YOUR SCORE 40

ASSISTANCE 40

TABLE OF CONTENTS

TAKING AN ACTION EVERY DAY 41

TELLING YOUR 100% STORY & MICHAEL'S 100%.................................42 - 43

MY 100 PERCENT STORY & JESSICA'S 100% ....44 - 45

PHASE ONE: FOCUS..**46 - 47**

MONTH 1: WEEK 1, 2, 3, 4, 5 ....48 - 65

MONTH 1 ....66 - 67

NOTES & TRIUMPHS ....68 - 69

PHASE TWO: MOMENTUM ....**70 - 71**

MONTH 2: WEEK 1, 2, 3, 4, 5 ....72 - 81

MONTH 2 ....82 - 83

NOTES & TRIUMPHS ....84 - 85

PHASE THREE - ACHIEVEMENT ....**86 - 90**

CHOOSE NOT TO BE COMMON 91

GOALS ....92 - 97

GOALS EXAMPLE ....98 - 99

GOAL 1 ....100 - 101

GOAL 1 NOTES ....102 - 103

MONTH 3: WEEK 1, 2, 3, 4, 5 ....104 - 113

MONTH 3 ....114 - 115

NOTES & TRIUMPHS ....116 - 117

MAINTENANCE ....118 - 119

GOAL 2 ....120 - 121

GOAL 2 NOTES ....122 - 123

GOAL 3 ....124 - 125

GOAL 3 NOTES ....126 - 127

ACTION PLAN EXAMPLE & FORM ....128 - 129

CONFERENCE CALL FORM ....130 - 131

ARE YOU READING? 132

ACKNOWLEDGEMENTS 133

INTRODUCTION

On the morning of Sunday, March 8, 2009 God dropped 30 DAYS AT 100 PERCENT into my Spirit as I was mulling over the fact that I wasn't 100%. You see, I realized something that I have known for awhile, that without doing my hair or makeup, or exercising my fat little growing tummy, planning out my day the night before, reading my Bible, praying on the regular, emptying out the dishes in the kitchen sink, and being able to sit down in my gray Ungaro skirt without choking, I am not 100%.

Having just completed Rick Warren's book *A Purpose Driven Life* with a small group of friends, I decided to share my idea with them. They all agreed that they too were not always 100%. We shared some ideas on what would make us 100%, and in a matter of hours we had resolved to meet together on the phone the next day in an effort to make 100% a way of life—30 days at a time.

We opened that phone call at 7:30AM on Monday, March 9, 2009 with a statement of what our 100% looked like to each of us. Everyones was different.

100% can mean one thing if you are a mom, something else if you are an investment banker, something different if you are a makeup artist, and yet another if you are an athlete. But regardless of who you are or what you do, EVERYONE has his or her own 100%, and at one time or another, we have all slacked off.

In my life, I find that the longer I slack off of my 100% the muddier things get and the more dominant my excuses become. That's because I'm now at 80% or even 70%, and I've bought into this new lower level of living with lower expectations.

Being at 100% means being ready for the 'everything and anything' opportunities that present themselves in your world, as well as the wonderful surprises that only those who are at 100% get to take advantage of.

How many times have you missed getting a great job, run into the perfect mate, or couldn't take advantage of a downturn in the stock market because you weren't 100%?

Still want to run out of the house without combing your hair, go to bed without cleaning the brushes in your makeup kit, or think you can graze over the notes for tomorrow's big meeting on the subway into work, and still shine like a star?

When you are striving to live at 100%, **you make different choices for your life** because 100% demands something new of you, and each new choice begets a new outcome that bonds you to a new routine which has its own momentum. Some people say they don't like routine. Who are they kidding? It's the routine that keeps you prepared for spontaneity. Order begets order, and produces the freedom to move, do and create. Can you remember the last time you felt 100%? Do you remember where you were? What you were wearing? Who you were with? What you were doing? Why you were there, and how you were feeling? Capture it! Take a picture of it in your mind. It's a mental and emotional record of your 100%.

Some people are really good at being able to visualize things they haven't seen or touched. That's amazing—and I'm working on getting better at it, but I've always been challenged with that kind of visualization.

As badly as I wanted that navy blue Range Rover with the beige leather interior and the navy blue piping, and as many times as I tried to imagine myself in the car driving it—(which I

did), I still couldn't quite wrap my head around the **feeling** of being in a car that I wasn't driving every day.

However, I could literally see myself walking into the Essence building at 1500 Broadway in New York City, slinging eight photography and styling portfolios, because I had done it so many times before. I can to this day experience the feeling of walking up to the receptionist and saying "Crystal Wright to see Mikki Garth-Taylor," the Beauty and Cover Editor at Essence magazine. I remember seeing her walk through that door to sit with me in the reception area, and the excitement of knowing that she didn't give just **anyone** an appointment.

That feeling of accomplishment is tied to everything about that moment. The way I was dressed, the way I sat, the way I shook her hand, the way I announced my name to the receptionist, the way she smiled at me and my **belief** that she must have thought "Crystal must have something really special in those portfolios to come all the way to New York to show them to me." It all made me feel FABULOUS. **And the energy in that moment of FABULOUS is my 100%.** I wanted it back. I wanted it every day. I wanted to recapture that feeling when I started writing 30 DAYS AT 100 PERCENT.

Join me on this 30-day journey back to capturing and keeping your 100%.

Sincerely,

Crystal A. Wright

Crystal A. Wright

30/100 PERCENT

INTRODUCTION

Welcome to 30 DAYS AT 100 PERCENT. Today is the day you take your power back.

THE LESSON

In September 1976 I moved into the Xavier Hall dorm at Seattle University weighing about 148 pounds. Pretty cute on a 5'11 frame! As was the tradition at Seattle University, during midterm and finals weeks, they wheeled around carts carrying hot cocoa and chocolate chip cookies. By February of the following year, I had gained 30 pounds.

And it wasn't just the hot cocoa, it was the entire college menu of meat, potatoes, bread, and sweets three times a day that my hips and I embraced. Add to that the fact that I was an athlete who hadn't played volleyball, basketball or run track since I graduated high school, and it won't take long to figure out what happened.

Before I knew it, four years had passed. It was 1980, I was now a student at the University of Washington, and I had added another 25 pounds, weighing in at a hefty 203. It was not cute. My mother once suggested that I try that new "exercise"—the push-away-and-close. "Push away from the table and close your mouth," she said. That's Mom.

It would have been okay, had I been okay with it, but I wasn't. I didn't realize it then but I would soon learn that I would never be truly happy or comfortable when I wasn't at least striving for 100%.

For the next three years I went up and down with my weight, went on crazy diets, and even took pills—you can get anything on a college campus.

I would lose 20 pounds in three weeks, and gain it back in a month. Lose it again and look good for a few weeks, and put it right back on.

When finally I resolved to do something about my weight, I knew for sure that cold turkey didn't work for me, and I really hated diets because the process of substituting everything in your food lifestyle with something completely different that you may not even like totally sets you up to fail.

I remember the first day as if it were yesterday. I looked in the mirror and said to myself, "You are better than this. **You are Frances Wilkinson's grandchild** and you can do better."

I put on a sweatshirt and pants—the same ones I didn't want to wear until I lost weight because they made me look fat—walked outside my apartment door and down the stairs, and started to run. I made it one-half block before I stopped, wheezing. It was baaadddd. I remember the day I discovered that my

INTRODUCTION

thighs were rubbing together in such a way—as if there is any other way—that I would rub the insides of my pant legs out. I had to keep taking my shoes to the shop to get the heels fixed because my body was too heavy for them. Ugh! It was awful.

MY FIRST 30 DAYS

So, four times a week for the first 30 days I ran half a block, and walked half a block, and ran half a block and walked half a block. I did that every other day. The half block became a block, then half a mile, a mile and then two. I started to feel better.

At the beginning of the second month, I added something new: Sweet-n-Low. I replaced sugar in everything except tea with Sweet-n-Low, again for a month. At the beginning of the third month, I replaced regular soda (I loved Coca-Cola, and still do) with Tab. Remember Tab? Tab had those really cool commercials where they wrapped a measuring tape around a glass and sucked it in like a waistline. Oops. Sorry! I digress.

At month four I replaced all of the white bread in my apartment with high-fiber wheat. I was amazed to find out that it had half the calories and tasted exactly the same. At month five I stopped eating after 7:30PM, had a cup of tea before every meal because it quelled my appetite, and stopped eating the MOMENT I felt full. Now you might be asking yourself, well how much weight had she lost? Honestly, I couldn't tell you, I never did get on a scale. I judged how well I was doing by my ability to wear the clothes in my closet that I loved, and how good that girl in the mirror looked and felt about reconnecting with the "she that she is" when she's bearing down on 100%.

In March of 2009 when I got the idea for 30 DAYS AT 100 PERCENT, I realized how many times in my life I have unknowingly used this 30 day method to get back in the saddle and make significant changes in my life. I'll share more stories with you later, but for now, the most important thing to remember is that NO ONE FALLS TO THE TOP.

Grab hold of those bootstraps and pull yourself up! Gather a couple of friends together if you are going to do the group thing, get on each others' calendar, and kick 60, 70, 80 and 90% in the butt on your way to 100%!

WHERE TO BEGIN

The process begins with an eye toward identifying your areas of opportunity, and then asks a few simple questions: What is my 100%? How would my life be different if I were striving to live at 100% every day? What actions am I willing to take to reach 100%?

As you move from day to day and week to week,

you begin to identify the distractions that keep you from reaching and maintaining your 100%. You are empowered by the positive changes that you are making, and begin to take control of the distractions, master the triggers, create new habits and embrace a new routine that supports your effort to reach and maintain 100% in your life.

THE BENEFITS OF BEING 100 PERCENT

Let me share what 30 DAYS AT 100 PERCENT has done for me. I feel FABULOUS again, joyous and giddy, in fact. I have more power because I have more energy, and I have more energy because I'm not running around like a chicken with its head cut off. My days have a beginning and an end. I have more time because I am removing the distractions that keep me enslaved to the mediocrity of a life not fully-lived. In other words, I'm cleaning up my act by taking charge of my life instead of letting things just happen to me.

Notice I said "removing," and not "removed." That's because life is a work in progress and tweaking is a part of life. What's working this year may not work as well next year because life is constantly in motion, and things change. That's when you tweak—make an adjustment, and keep it movin'!

When I turned 48, all kinds of weird things started happening to my body. First it was the need for Glucosamine and MSM for my poor achin' bones.

At 50 I called my Mom and said, "What the heck is going on? I'm hot!" She informed me that I was having hot flashes. "Oh no!" I said. "I'm not ready! It's a cruel joke," I told her, "to look like you're 35 and feel like you're 55."

I had to make some adjustments fast, and one of those was adding an herbal supplement to my daily routine. Ugh! And whenever I thought I didn't have to take that supplement, I paid for it by getting steamy—and not in a positive way. At the worst possible time I would break out into a sweat. After it happened a few times, I finally resolved to get my act together, add it into my routine and keep it movin'.

Striving for 100% will make you feel awesome. You'll take your power back, and the energy to do and create will come back, because all of the time you've lost by being at 70% returns when you are at 100%.

Self-determination and self esteem are the by-products of making good personal and professional decisions. You feel alive, special and blessed. You feel like the deck is stacked in your favor, and that you are in more control of the outcomes in your life. You feel ready. You feel sure of your decision-making because you are prepared. None of it is magic. It's something you've probably heard, "success is what happens when opportunity knocks and you are prepared to receive it."

INTRODUCTION

WHAT HAPPENED TO MY 100%

I needed to figure out what had happened to my 100%; when and where had I lost the will to strive for, and be, the best that I could be?

I found it in the resolve of having an uncluttered kitchen after the last glass and saucer in the dish rack had been put away.

I found it in my closet after I had reorganized it by item, color and length so that getting dressed was no longer an ordeal and an excuse for being late to a business meeting or dinner with friends.

I found it on the floor in my living room after the exhilaration of my 50th sit-up and 30th push-up.

I found it being of service at an elementary school in Compton, California where Fleacé and I volunteered with folks from other churches and community organizations to help paint the portable classrooms [in an underserved community] early one Saturday morning.

I found it in the bathroom mirror after curling my hair, perfecting my brows, lashes, cheeks and lips, and dabbing on a bit of perfume because it made me feel beautiful and sexy.

I found it in my Apple iPhone after it reminded me that I had an appointment with a potential client three days in advance, so that I could prepare like a pro instead of making an excuse for why my presentation lacked pizzazz.

MAINTAINING 100 PERCENT

You see, 100% demands that you eliminate, minimize, or remove from your presence those things that distract you to the point that you lose your focus.

If seeing dirty dishes in the sink in the morning takes you off of your game like it does me, do them at night before you go to bed, so that you begin every day with a fresh new slate. Allowing "it" to happen repeatedly when you know its effect on you means that you are CHOOSING to be less than 100%. You are giving the dishes the power to keep you from achieving something much more important.

It seems too simple, doesn't it? But we do it every day. Instead of giving ourselves the four hours that we know we will need to get ready for the big meeting, we choose to clean out the closet for two hours, knowing full well that we'll never be at our tip-top best with only two hours of preparation.

What about the traffic excuse? Instead of leaving the house at 2:15PM to get across town by 3:00PM, we don't leave until 2:30PM or 2:45PM, and then we curse every other driver on the street for making *us* late. Stop the madness!

30/100 PERCENT

INTRODUCTION

HOW 30 DAYS WORKS

As I said earlier, 30 DAYS AT 100 PERCENT is broken into three phases:

The first 30 DAYS is FOCUS. During the Focus phase we figure out what happened to our 100% by going through a series of short exercises that force us to identify what being 100% looks and feels like in all 8 areas of our life.

The second 30 DAYS is MOMENTUM. During the Momentum phase we hit our stride and get comfortable with our new routine. It's here that we really start taking our power back and get control of our precious time.

ACHIEVEMENT, the last 30 days, is where we find the space and power to set new goals for ourselves that can be accomplished with the new discipline we have incorporated into our lives during the previous 60 days.

So check this out. Every day starts at 100%. Think about it. Isn't that great? You wake up every morning at 100%. Now what you do with that 100% is up to you, and it's completely dependent upon the daily actions that you take to achieve 100% in a single area and category of your choice, each 30 days! (See pages 128-129 for an example of my daily action plan.)

If you set a goal or intended to take an action that you didn't accomplish but you gave it your all, then you're still at 100%. However, if you set a goal that you didn't accomplish because you spent half the day talking to your friends on Facebook, well that's a different story, isn't it?

I'm sure that most of us would agree that these social networking sites have their benefits, but come on, half of us are well on our way to carpal tunnel syndrome from pounding the refresh button on our laptop computers because we can't wait 30 seconds for the next set of Facebook messages to appear on the screen. Really now, we've taken impatience to a whole new level.

At the end of the day when you're sitting down with your workbook assessing how you fared against the targets that you set for yourself, you are the one who decides whether you are at 70, 82, 95 or 100 percent. This is the honor system. You are accountable to YOU.

Every night before you go to bed, you will take the time to write a 3-line synopsis of the day with a corresponding percentage. At the end of the week, you'll total up the percentages for each day and divide by 7—the number of days in the week. The resulting number is your week's average, between 0 and 100%.

Next you'll find four simple questions that you will answer at the end of each week. How do

INTRODUCTION

you feel about the week? What could you have done differently? What will you do differently next week? Will you add anything new next week?

A CIRCLE OF FRIENDS

30 DAYS AT 100 PERCENT is designed so that you can do it alone, or with a very small group of friends. Everyone works differently. With the right person, or people—it can be nice to have others around to encourage you to stay on top of your game, and you can do the same for them. However success is not always a team sport. When I was 55 pounds overweight it didn't take me long to figure out that if I waited for my friends to work out with me, I might be waiting forever. So go for it, with partners or without. Either way is fine!

If you can find one or two people that you know have the same level of commitment and are willing to put forth the same effort that you are prepared to invest, invite them to do 30 DAYS with you. However, (and this is very important), allow no more than three people in your group at a time, and choose people you trust, respect, even love. I call it "A Circle of Friends."

Why no more than three? Because the more people you add, the greater the possibility that you will include a hater—someone who doesn't like you, or is jealous of you! Most of us don't want to share our personal stuff with strangers, so keep your group small, and tight.

30 DAYS AT 100 PERCENT is about commitment—sticking to it, accountability—showing up for yourself first, and then for others if you are in a group, and responsibility—keeping your big mouth shut about other peoples' stuff.

As my friend Mosi likes to remind me when I start running off at the mouth, "Crystal," she says, "you're at a 27, I need you to be at a 13". That means, bring it down a notch!

As a rule, if you approach someone about joining you for 30 days, and they give you too much resistance, drop it or you'll end up on that conference call all by yourself. Not because they can't get their booty out of bed for a 20 minute phone call, but because they simply are not ready to change their lives right now!

You cannot drag someone kicking and screaming to success. You can try, but it's your arms that will be aching at the end of that rope—not theirs. I have a few people in my life I would like to save, too. However, our dream for others is not always their dream for themselves.

It doesn't mean that they won't come around, but like church, sometimes the easiest way to get someone to go, is when they witness the positive changes in your life and attitude. For now, if they don't want to come, don't make 'em.

WORKIN' THE PLAN

STEP 1: WHAT TO DO FIRST

Decide whether you are going it alone or in a group. If you are flying solo, skip to page 20, Step 3. If the group route suits you read on.

1) Use the spaces below to create a short list of people you would enjoy making this journey with.

2) Make a few phone calls and see who's up for joining your circle. There are lots of folks who are not 100%, but would like to be. Just ask!

3) Encourage each member to pick up 30 DAYS by visiting **30DaysAt100Percent.com**.

4) If you brought the group together, log into freeconferencecall.com, get and share the phone and pin number with your group.

THE SHORT LIST

1 ....
2 ....
3 ....
4 ....
5 ....

Conference calls are very important for the group in the first 30 days, they promote accountability. Schedule 2 in weeks 1 and 2, and *at least* 1 in weeks 3 and 4. Beyond that, you decide.

STEP 2: CONFERENCE CALLS

Set up a time for the initial conference call. On that call you will:

1) Discuss a name for your circle, and write it in the space provided at right. ▶ ▶ ▶

3) Decide what day and time you will gather for the once or twice weekly conference calls and record it at right. ▶ ▶ ▶

4) Decide how long the calls will be. No call should be longer than 30 minutes. ▶ ▶ ▶

5) Talk briefly about the two questions that will be answered and discussed on the first conference call:

Q 1: What does MY 100% look like?

Action: Each person will be expected to take turns reading from their completed AREAS OF OPPORTUNITY list, one at a time.

Q 2: What item from MY 100% Personal and/or MY 100% Professional will I tackle in the first month?

Action: Each person will be expected to identify the items they will attack in month 1, how it will be done and how they will benefit from reaching focus in their lives.

WORKIN' THE PLAN

30/100 PERCENT

CIRCLE

FREE CONFERENCE CALL.COM NO:

_____
PHONE NUMBER

_____
PIN NUMBER

_____
DAY & TIME

_____
CALL LENGTH

NAME...
RELATIONSHIP:.................................
    CO-WORKER, FRIEND, FAMILY, SPOUSE
PHONE:...
EMAIL:..

NAME...
RELATIONSHIP:.................................
    CO-WORKER, FRIEND, FAMILY, SPOUSE
PHONE:...
EMAIL:..

NAME...
RELATIONSHIP:.................................
    CO-WORKER, FRIEND, FAMILY, SPOUSE
PHONE:...
EMAIL:..

THOUGHTS & OBSERVATIONS

....
....
....
....
....
....
....
....
....
....
....
....
....
....
....
....
....
....
....
....
....
....
....
....
....
....
....
....

30/100 PERCENT

WORKIN' THE PLAN

STEP 3: TAKE INVENTORY

30 DAYS challenges you to identify your own personal 100% in 8 different areas of your life: Inside, Outside, Personal, Professional, Family, Finances, Activities and Health. You do that, by completing a very simple sentence: "I am 100% when....."

For example, looking on the facing page at an **AREA** like, **FINANCES**, there is Checking, Savings, Investments and Credit. Finishing the sentence might look like this:

> I am 100% when my checking account balance is $1500 each month.
> I am 100% when I save $350 each month.
> I am 100% when my credit score is 750.
> I am 100% when I invest $200 or more each quarter in tech stocks.

The program contains both a **Personal**, and a **Professional** section. For purposes of explanation, take a moment to review the AREAS, and CATEGORIES in the Personal section below:

AREAS	CATEGORIES
INSIDE	Emotional, Spiritual, Mental...
OUTSIDE	Face, Body, Hair...
PERSONAL	Friends, Mate...
PROFESSIONAL	Work, Promotion, Education...
FAMILY	Siblings, Parents, Relationships
FINANCES	Checking, Savings, Credit
ACTIVITIES	Hobbies, Socializing...
HEALTH	Fitness, Checkups, Dental...

Not sure what I mean yet? Listen, if your credit score is 500 and you are having problems getting a decent interest rate to purchase a car, this will give you an opportunity to utilize the category "Credit" in your FINANCES Area.

If you believe that your teeth are keeping you from getting a better job, promotion, or a new mate, then make "Dental" one of the categories in your HEALTH Area.

On the facing page is a sampling of what makes me 100% (CRYSTAL'S AREAS OF OPPORTUNITY). My lists will give you a good example of what to do with yours on P22-25. ▶ ▶ ▶

STEP 4: FILL IN THE BLANKS

It's your turn. Grab a beverage, turn to P22-25, sit back in a chair, and take the time to:

1) Review and think about the Categories that should fit within each of the **AREAS** (Outside, Inside, Personal, Health, Finances, etc.).

   Change the "Categories" to whatever is important to you. That's why I greyed them out, and left extra spaces.

2) Now, fill in the blanks of your own "Areas of Opportunity." Maybe you have a significant other, and you think that Relationship ought to be an **AREA** so you can work on achieving 100% in certain categories. That's fine. Go for it!

AREAS OF OPPORTUNITY
PERSONAL INVENTORY OF WHAT IS WORKING & WHAT I NEED TO WORK ON

30/100 PERCENT

I AM 100% WHEN.....

OUTSIDE

FACE	My brows, lashes, cheeks & lips are ready for prime time.
BODY	My tummy is flat.
HAIR	My hair is cut into a style so that when it is curled it stays, is bouncy and behavin'.
HANDS & FEET	My fingernails are filled. I have no broken nails, my feet are soft and my pedicure is less than a week and a half old.

INSIDE

SPIRITUALITY	I spend at least 30 minutes each morning in the Word reading my Bible.
MENTAL	I make time each week to read 1-2 chapters of a great book.
EMOTIONAL	

FINANCES

CHECKING	My checking account balance average is $1,500 each month.
SAVINGS	I am saving $350 each month
CREDIT	My credit score is 750
INVESTMENTS	I invest a minimum of $200 each quarter in a tech stock

HEALTH

FITNESS	My tummy is flat, my arms are tight, and I can breathe when sitting down in my Gray Ungaro skirt.
DOCTOR VISITS	
DENTIST	My teeth are healthy and bright white.
VITAMINS	I remember to take my Glucosamine and MSM each morn.

30/100 PERCENT

I AM 100% WHEN.....

INSIDE

...............SPIRITUAL

...............MENTAL

...........EMOTIONAL

_____
_____
_____
_____
_____
_____

OUTSIDE

...............FACE

...............BODY

...............HAIR

.........HANDS & FEET

_____
_____
_____
_____
_____

PERSONAL

...............FAMILY

...............FRIENDS

_____
_____
_____
_____
_____
_____

PROFESSIONAL

...............WORK

...........PROMOTION

_____
_____
_____
_____
_____

MY
AREAS OF OPPORTUNITY
PERSONAL INVENTORY OF WHAT IS WORKING & WHAT I NEED TO WORK ON

30/100
PERCENT

I AM 100% WHEN.....

FAMILY
.............SIBLINGS
.............PARENTS
.............CHILDREN
.............RELATIONSHIPS

_____
_____
_____
_____
_____
_____
_____

FINANCES
.............CHECKING
.............SAVINGS
.............RETIREMENT
.............CREDIT

_____
_____
_____
_____
_____

ACTIVITIES
.............HOBBIES

.............SOCIALIZING

.............CHARITY

_____
_____
_____
_____
_____

HEALTH
.............FITNESS
.............DOCTOR
.............DENTIST
.............WEIGHT

_____
_____
_____
_____

30/100 PERCENT

MY
AREAS OF OPPORTUNITY
PROFESSIONAL INVENTORY OF WHAT IS WORKING & WHAT I NEED TO WORK ON

I AM 100% WHEN.....

EMPLOYMENT

............CAREER

..................JOB

............INTERVIEWS

..........RELOCATION

ADVANCEMENT

STRATEGIC PLANNING

............PROMOTION

.........NETWORKING

SKILLS

.SELF-IMPROVEMENT

...............TRAINING

.........EDUCATION

COMPENSATION

..............SALARY

.......COMMISSIONS

............OVERTIME

............BENEFITS

MY
AREAS OF OPPORTUNITY
PROFESSIONAL INVENTORY OF WHAT IS WORKING & WHAT I NEED TO WORK ON

PERFORMANCE

I AM 100% WHEN.....

...............% OF PLAN
_____
_____
...............PERKS
_____
_____
_____
_____
_____

WORK ENVIRONMENT

...............CULTURE
_____
_____
...............ATMOSPHERE
_____
_____
...............RELATIONSHIPS
_____
_____

REST

...............VACATION
_____
_____
...............HOLIDAYS
_____
_____
_____

PROMOTION

...............RAISE
_____
_____
...............JOB TITLE
_____
_____
_____

WORKIN' THE PLAN

Now that you have addressed each of the categories in your PERSONAL INVENTORY by completing the sentence "I am 100% when.." did you experience any surprises? If something jumped out at you, jot it down.

SURPRISES

1. ....
....
....
....
....
....
....

2. ....
....
....
....
....
....

3. ....
....
....
....
....
....
....

Were you surprised at how many areas you were already at or close to 100%? The good news is, every area where you are 100% leaves you more time to focus on the areas that really need your attention. Below are more examples, some personal, others professional.

FAMILY	I AM 100% WHEN.....
WIFE	I make a date with my wife each week
SON	I play basketball w/my son after work
DAUGHTER	I get home in time to tuck my daughter into bed.

EMPLOYMENT	I AM 100% WHEN.....
JOB	I have a clearly defined job description and expectations that I can meet and exceed.
CAREER	I can see the path to my next promotion.
NETWORKING	I see every business encounter as an interview for upward mobility.

OUTSIDE	I AM 100% WHEN.....
FACE	My brows, lashes, cheeks and lips are ready for prime time
BODY	I weigh 153 lbs.
HANDS/FEET	My nails are beautifully painted, my feet are soft, and my pedicure is less than a week and a half old.

TRAINING	I AM 100% WHEN.....
COMPANY EDUCATION	I take advantage of company offered courses that provide opportunities to add skills for advancement.
COURSES	I take 1-2 short courses each year to enhance my marketability.

WORKIN' THE PLAN

STEP 5: REVIEW

Review what you've written down in your **AREAS** of Opportunity. Looks pretty amazing on paper doesn't it? Gives you a chance to see how far off of the 100% mark you are.

And this is where we all get into trouble. We evaluate our lives all the time. We do it with to do lists, daily reminders, and new years resolutions. The problem is, that we try to fix everything at once, and when it doesn't happen, we get upset, frustrated, and often throw in the towel all together. Rome wasn't built in a day, but we think we're going to start going to the gym every day, set up a date night with our spouse, make it home in time to tuck our kids in to bed, take a class at the university, start saving $300 a month, and get up an hour earlier to invest in the stock market before we take a shower to go to work.

Does it sound reasonable? No, it sounds nuts. And that is why you are going to choose 1, maybe 2 categories from your AREAS to work on in the first 30 days. Trust me, the second 30 days will be here soon enough!

1) Return to P22-25. Use a highlighter to identify 1 - 2 CATEGORIES and the corresponding "I AM 100% WHEN."

STEP 6: RECORD

Turn this page and take a look at how I completed Crystal's 100 Percent. Your 100 Percent [for the first 30 days] should be **one** item in a personal category, (and maybe one in a professional category) that [when done properly and **consistently**] makes you feel prepared, happy, healthy, fulfilled, and ready for anything. Once turned into habit, these accomplishments will set the stage for you to tackle some big goals in your life in the Achievement phase of this program.

1) Transfer those 1-2 highlighted CATEGORIES and I AM 100% WHEN on P22-25 that you will work on, to P30 & 32.

2) On P31 & 33, write a brief statement of "How" you will do it.

For example, if saving $400 each month is your 100%, ask yourself, "How am I going to do it?" A great "How" might sound like this: At 7PM every Friday, I will transfer $100 from my checking account into my savings account after receiving my payroll check. It's better to transfer $100 every Friday than to do it once a month. The weekly action creates the habit!

3) Add the Payoff, the benefits that you will gain by striving for and achieving 100%.

Trust me, you're not doing any of this stuff unless there's a payoff. You know it, and I know it!

CRYSTAL'S 100 PERCENT

CHOOSE 1 PERSONAL/PROF. ITEM THAT YOU WILL FOCUS ON EACH MONTH

MY 100 PERCENT

1ST 30 DAYS: FOCUS
AREA: OUTSIDE   CATEGORY: FACE, BODY, HAIR

I AM 100 PERCENT WHEN: *My brows lashes cheeks lips and hair are ready for prime time.*

HOW WILL YOU DO IT: *I master my outward appearance by tweezing my brows at night b4 bed and getting up 20 minutes earlier in the morning.*

2ND 30 DAYS: MOMENTUM
AREA: ADVANCEMENT   CATEGORY: STRATEGIC PLANNING

I AM 100 PERCENT WHEN: *I have written down my plan for achieving the targets necessary for becoming the general manager at my company in 1 year.*

HOW WILL YOU DO IT: *By introducing and implementing new processes and procedures at the company that will impact the bottom line and position me as a leader.*

3RD 30 DAYS: ACHIEVEMENT
AREA: TRAINING   CATEGORY: ADVANCED EDUCATION

I AM 100 PERCENT WHEN: *I seek out and secure management courses that expand my knowledge and opportunities to give me an edge.*

HOW WILL YOU DO IT: *By visiting the web at the beginning of each month to find out what's being offered and opening up my schedule for classes.*

CRYSTAL'S 100% PAYOFF

WRITE DOWN SEVERAL BENEFITS THAT YOU WILL RECEIVE FROM REACHING 100%

THE PAYOFF

1ST 30 DAYS: FOCUS

▶ 1) Because I look and feel finished, complete and at my very best, I feel good about running
▶ into friends, colleagues, and meeting new people.
▶ 2) Because I have my act together on the outside, I attract more attention from potential
▶ clients who want to know who does my hair and makeup.
▶ 3) When I look professional, I feel professional.
▶
▶

2ND 30 DAYS: MOMENTUM

▶ 1) I am always prepared.
▶ 2) I feel ready for anything.
▶ 3) I am ready to take advantage of opportunities.
▶ 4) I have a roadmap for how I'm going to get from point A to point B.
▶ 5) I am looked at by my superiors as a candidate for promotion.

3RD 30 DAYS: ACHIEVEMENT

▶ 1) I will learn how to reach a wider audience of potential clients who are in need of educa-
▶ tional services that teach their students how to find work once they graduate from makeup,
▶ hair or fashion school.
▶ 2) I will be able to craft a better more efficient and captivating message that extolls the bene-
▶ fits of the Crystal Wright Live brand to prospective clients.
▶ 3) I will teach my staff how to share instead of sell the benefits of the CWL brand.

MY 100 PERCENT

MY 100 PERCENT

1ST 30 DAYS: FOCUS

AREA: _____ CATEGORY: _____ ▶

1) I AM 100% WHEN _____ ▶

_____ ▶

_____

HOW WILL YOU DO IT: _____ ▶

_____ ▶

_____ ▶

_____ ▶

2ND 30 DAYS: MOMENTUM

AREA: _____ CATEGORY: _____ ▶

1) I AM 100% WHEN _____ ▶

_____ ▶

_____ ▶

HOW WILL YOU DO IT: _____ ▶

_____ ▶

_____ ▶

_____ ▶

3RD 30 DAYS: ACHIEVEMENT

AREA: _____ CATEGORY: _____ ▶

1) I AM 100% WHEN _____ ▶

_____ ▶

_____

HOW WILL YOU DO IT: _____ ▶

_____ ▶

_____ ▶

MY 100% PAYOFF

WRITE DOWN SEVERAL BENEFITS THAT YOU WILL RECEIVE FROM REACHING 100%

THE PAYOFF

1ST 30 DAYS: FOCUS

▶ _____
▶ _____
▶ _____
▶ _____
▶ _____
▶ _____
▶ _____
▶ _____

2ND 30 DAYS: MOMENTUM

▶ _____
▶ _____
▶ _____
▶ _____
▶ _____
▶ _____
▶ _____
▶ _____

3RD 30 DAYS: ACHIEVEMENT

▶ _____
▶ _____
▶ _____
▶ _____
▶ _____
▶ _____
▶ _____

MY 100 PERCENT

CHOOSE 1 PROFESSIONAL ITEM THAT YOU WILL FOCUS ON EACH MONTH

MY 100 PERCENT

1ST 30 DAYS: FOCUS

AREA: _____ CATEGORY: _____

1) I AM 100% WHEN _____

_____

_____

HOW WILL YOU DO IT: _____

_____

_____

_____

2ND 30 DAYS: MOMENTUM

AREA: _____ CATEGORY: _____

1) I AM 100% WHEN _____

_____

_____

HOW WILL YOU DO IT: _____

_____

_____

_____

3RD 30 DAYS: ACHIEVEMENT

AREA: _____ CATEGORY: _____

1) I AM 100% WHEN _____

_____

_____

HOW WILL YOU DO IT: _____

_____

_____

_____

MY 100% PAYOFF

WRITE DOWN SEVERAL BENEFITS THAT YOU WILL RECEIVE FROM REACHING 100%

THE PAYOFF

1ST 30 DAYS: FOCUS

▶ _____
▶ _____
▶ _____
▶ _____
▶ _____
▶ _____
▶ _____
▶ _____

2ND 30 DAYS: MOMENTUM

▶ _____
▶ _____
▶ _____
▶ _____
▶ _____
▶ _____
▶ _____
▶ _____

3RD 30 DAYS: ACHIEVEMENT

▶ _____
▶ _____
▶ _____
▶ _____
▶ _____
▶ _____
▶ _____

30/100 PERCENT

WORKIN' THE PLAN

EVERY DAY AT 100 PERCENT

30 DAYS AT 100 PERCENT begs the question: How would MY life be different if I were striving to live at 100%? What is the outcome—the big payoff?

Use me as an example. From my **AREAS** of Opportunity on P21, I select OUTSIDE, and the category is FACE. This is the ONE thing I commit to tackling in the first 30 days. I've written it on P28, in the section titled CRYSTAL'S 100%.

It may not seem like a big deal to you, but when you have been a slacker for nearly a year, exercising that muscle of doing your makeup everyday, is a chore until' it becomes a habit again. This was me in March 09. I didn't want to get overwhelmed—do too much. It's not a race. Do not compete with your friends, significant other, family or colleagues.

Compare the action to working out. If you haven't been to the gym in awhile, just about the worst thing you can do is attempt 200 sit-ups on your first day back. You may get it done, but if you are wracked with aches and pains, will you want to go back to the gym on day two? Probably not. That's why no matter how many people sign up for gym memberships, there is always plenty of room to work out. Most people obliterate themselves and their will to succeed on the first day and they never return. We're not going that route.

To the right of CRYSTAL'S 100 PERCENT is THE PAYOFF—what you gain. As the weeks go on and you consistently master an item—let's say that keeping your calendar up-to-date proves to be so rewarding and much easier to commit to than you thought—you may decide to add something else from an AREA of Opportunity. However, don't feel compelled to do so. Like poker, it's okay to HOLD. You can add something new next month.

It took me three years to lose 55 pounds, and I did it by incorporating one or two new habits into my life—30 days at a time. Remember, it takes 21 days to create a new habit when you act consciously and consistently. The other nine days are for insurance.

By consistently striving for and performing at 100%, you can begin to tackle and achieve some pretty important goals in your life...and we will, 30 Days at a time!

STEP 7: MASTERING TRIGGERS & CONTROLS

Now that you know what would make you 100%, lets take the blinders off, and pull the sheets back off of the things and/or people that you have been allowing to keep you from being your very best.

Early in the book, I said "Triggers are the things that take you off your game, and Controls are the things that you put in place to get you back on track. Some of mine follow.

For instance, here's a **TRIGGER**: Answering the phone during my morning prayer time causes me to lose my place and my focus, and I don't get the direction that I need to go about my day.

Now, here's the **CONTROL**: When I wake in the morning, I unplug the landline before I make my coffee, and I turn the ringer off on my cell phone for the first 90 minutes of my day.

TRIGGER: If I have an apple martini at night when I have something important to read or work on, I get sleepy and lethargic.

CONTROL: Instead of an apple martini, I pour myself a glass of Chardonnay. It doesn't have the same effect on me, and inevitably, there's still a bit in the bottom of the glass when I call it quits at midnight. I haven't had an apple martini at home on a weeknight since September 2009. How's that for CONTROL?!

TRIGGER: When I start my day by checking my email, I get sidetracked. Before I know it, an hour has passed and I'm 45 minutes behind on my day. Sound familiar?

CONTROL: I do not check my email until I'm showered, my hair and makeup are done, I am completely dressed, I've completed my exercises, and I'm on my 2nd cup of coffee.

TRIGGER: Leaving dishes in the sink or clutter in my bathroom makes me feel disorganized and distracted, which compels me to set aside really important things in order to straighten up, fix or clean, when I should be focused on something that really matters—like writing a new book.

CONTROL: I make an effort to put things back in their proper place in the kitchen whenever I use them during the day. I make sure to wash all the dirty dishes and glasses, and clean my countertops before I go to bed.

TRIGGER: Saying "yes" to things without consulting my calendar causes me to over-commit, and under-deliver. I apologize, but then feel the need to do something to make up for the screw up, which makes me over-commit and under-deliver.

CONTROL: I do not commit to anything without having my calendar in front of me, and I ask people to send me email requests so that I remember to add important events to my calendar when I get to my office.

You see, once you've identified the things that take you off your 100%, you can no longer say "Oh, I didn't know that would happen." Now, it's your turn, flip to the next page and,

1) Write down the Triggers that take you off your game, and the Controls that you will put in place and use to take your power back.

TRIGGERS & CONTROLS

TRIGGERS	**CONTROLS**
THE THINGS THAT TAKE ME OFF MY GAME	WHAT I'M GOING TO DO ABOUT IT

1. ....
....
....
....

2. ....
....
....
....

3. ....
....
....
....

4. ....
....
....
....

5. ....
....
....
....

1. ....
....
....
....

2. ....
....
....
....

3. ....
....
....
....

4. ....
....
....
....

5. ....
....
....
....

TRIGGERS & CONTROLS

TRIGGERS

THE THINGS THAT TAKE ME OFF MY GAME

6 ....

....

....

....

7. ....

....

....

....

8. ....

....

....

....

9. ....

....

....

....

10 . ...

....

....

....

CONTROLS

WHAT I'M GOING TO DO ABOUT IT

6 ....

....

....

....

7. ....

....

....

....

8. ....

....

....

....

9. ....

....

....

....

10 . ...

....

....

....

30/100 PERCENT

WORKIN' THE PLAN

THOUGHTS & OBSERVATIONS

....
....
....
....
....
....
....
....
....
....
....
....
....
....
....
....
....
....
....
....
....
....
....
....

STEP 8: PREPARATION

Contemplate the 2 questions on P39 that you will answer on the first conference call. If you are not in a group, set aside some time on the morning of the first day to review the 1-2 things that you will focus on in month one.

On the night before the second conference call, turn to page 50 (Conference call 2 Week 1), answer the questions, and be prepared to discuss them on the conference call the following morning.

If you are flying solo, do the same exercise, using the same forms, just have the conversation with yourself. Review your progress and plan your strategy accordingly.

After the second week, it's fine to go to one conference call instead of two. It's up to you. Do what feels right.

If you find after a few days that you added to much (working on 2 categories instead of 1), dial it back. Take one out, and keep it moving. Remember, it's your 100% and it takes a minute to get it right.

If you started with only one thing, and find that you can do more, add something from your **AREAS OF OPPORTUNITY** to **MY 100%**, write in **THE PAYOFF**, and keep it moving.

CONFERENCE CALL 1 WEEK 1

NO CROSS TALK. NO FIXING OTHER PEOPLES' CHALLENGES. NO INTERRUPTIONS EXCEPT FOR A TIME STAMP. WHAT HAPPENS ON THE CALL STAYS ON THE CALL.

QUESTION 1:

What does your 100% look like?

GROUP EXERCISE 1: Refer to pages 22-25

ACTION: Each person should take turns and read from their completed AREAS OF OPPORTUNITY list, one area at a time.

Ex: OUTSIDE. I'm 100% when.......
INSIDE. I'm 100% when
PERSONAL. I'm 100% when, etc...

QUESTION 2:

What item(s) from MY 100% Personal and/or MY 100% Professional will you tackle in the first 30 days?

GROUP EXERCISE 2: Refer to pages 30-33.

ACTION: Each person should take turns and read from MY 100% Personal and/or Professional those 1-2 items from their Areas that they are going to tackle, making sure to include each building block:

1. AREA
2. CATEGORY
3. I AM 100% WHEN
4. HOW
5. PAYOFF

Do not overdo it! I'll say it again, it is not a race. Your life didn't get out of whack in a week. You're not going to put it all back together in seven days. Remember, Plan to Work & Work the Plan!

Creating new habits takes time, however the rewards can and will be GREAT!

1) ....
....
....
....
....
....
....
....
....
....
....

2) ....
....
....
....
....
....
....
....
....

WORKIN' THE PLAN

STEP 9: YOUR STORY

At some point over the next few weeks I want you to write your own "MY 100% STORY" in the space provided on page 44. It's the script of your life as you would like to play it out. Come on, we do it all the time. Haven't you ever started daydreaming, and when you didn't like the way the story unfolded, you hit rewind on the remote control in your mind and started the daydream over until it was just perfect?

Kobe Bryant never out-maneuvers you in the NBA playoff day dream; Brad Pitt always picks you instead of Angelina Jolie in *Mr. and Mrs. Smith*; and you really were a Bond Girl in that last *007* movie with Daniel Craig.

All I am suggesting is that if you can daydream a romance with a movie star, you can create the life that you desire right now by committing to paper the best you, that you can be, and then taking action!

Study that YOU. Walk in those shoes. And then step by step manifest the life that you desire—30 DAYS AT A TIME.

STEP 10: WHAT'S YOUR SCORE

One of the most fun aspects of 30 Days at 100% is keeping score. I talked about it at the beginning of the book on page 16. But let me break it down for you in 3 simple steps.

1) Turn to P48, and write a 3 line synopsis (about what you would twitter) about your day.

Was it good? Bad? Did you control it? Did it control you? Were you movin' and groovin', or did an old trigger get the best of you?

> Ex: I was on fire today. Closed a deal with Brenner School for 100 books. Got to all my appointments on time. Didn't make it to the gym so I walked 1.5 miles.

2) Write in your percentage.

Were you 87%, 92%, 66%? You are accountable to yourself.

3) At the end of the week, total up your percentages and divide by 7.

> Ex: 72% + 81% + 98% + 92% + 65% + 88% + 80% = 576 / 7 = 82%

Taking the time to record your percentage will give you a target to aim for week after week!

ASSISTANCE

People who strive for 100% know that they ARE their choices. Better choices beget better outcomes, and if you stick with it, progress is part of the process.

As you go through the process, if you find that

WORKIN' THE PLAN

you need help, support, guidance, clarification or just a big push, you can connect with me on my blog at:

livinglifeat100percent.com/blog

email me at:

crystal@crystalwrightlive.com

or sign up in our online community at:

30daysat100percent.ning.com

I want to hear about your successes, coach where I can, and help you find new ways to cultivate a 100% mindset that places you mentally inside the life of your choosing.

We can meet the challenges you encounter together, as a team, and as a community. When you reach your 100% you will find like-minded people who, like you, have committed to excellence both professionally and personally.

AN ACTION EVERY DAY

At the end of the day, the most important thing is to ask yourself, "What actions am I willing to take in order to reach my 100%?" Because just thinking about it won't make it happen. You're going to have to commit. More importantly, you are going to have to DO SOMETHING! Every Single Day!

If you can only change one thing a month, then do it. One thing a month is 12 things a year. Imagine today how different your life will be in one year, if you make 12 changes. It's phenomenal.

At the end of each week, after you've assessed your commitment and resolved to start the next week still committed to being 100%, think about Tiger Woods in one of his red shirts, winning one of his many championships and give yourself one of those open mouth, 'fist in the air' moments, scream out loud, and then, do it all over again!

NOTES

....
....
....
....
....
....
....
....
....
....
....
....
....
....
....
....

30/100 PERCENT
TELLING YOUR 100% STORY

As you go back over and review everything you've written on the preceding four pages (Areas of Opportunity, My 100 Percent and The Payoff), start thinking about your own 100% story. It may take two days or two weeks to write that story. Why? Because rarely does 100% come from a single moment in time. Even my "firing on all cylinders" Essence moment would have to be put in the professional column of my life. There are many life moments that I string together to weave my own 100% story, including a seminar that I presented several years ago in Los Angeles.

I remember it clearly. It was the rowdiest one-day class that I have ever conducted. My attendees and I were one! They were connecting with me. I was connecting with them. They were connecting with each other. It was magical. That class IS my gold standard. It's the space that I want everyone to be in when they choose me as their success coach. That experience has happened many times since then, but I didn't realize that I could duplicate every aspect of that day until I started writing 30 DAYS AT 100 PERCENT.

Telling the story, and recounting the details of what made that day perfect and special makes it possible for me to recreate, and stage that part of my life over, and over again. Filmmakers do it in the movies all the time, only they call it a script. Then they hire a bunch of folks to set—you guessed it—the stage!

Your 100%, like mine, may come from several different places, times, and dates. Recalling them may take some time. That's cool. We've got at least 30 days.

What if you find yourself with very few or no 100% moments that you can recall? Don't worry about it. Write your own script with moments that you create in your head. It's your life.

Gather the Who, What, Where, Why, When, and How of your script and apply them to your personal and professional life, inside and out; health, money, home and leisure, etc. That picture will become the script of your fabulous life at 100%!

In April, I gave 30 DAYS AT 100 PERCENT to a few friends, who started using it and having success with it right away. Michael Norville is one of those friends. One evening he read his 100% story to me, which moved me to make space for yours. For inspiration check out page 43, and read Michael's story.

If you get stuck telling your story, ask yourself these questions about each area: Who was I with? What was I doing? Where was I? Why was I there? When was it, and how did I feel?

How you feel is crucial, because inherent in this process is creating, or recreating and capturing feelings of success, happiness, confidence, and smarts. Quite simply—fabulousness.

Use pages 44 and 45 to complete your own 100% story.

MICHAEL'S 100 PERCENT

BY MICHAEL NORVILLE, LOS ANGELES, CALIFORNIA

At 100% I'm completely in the flow and connected to God. I actually hear the voice of Inspiration. If I'm listening to a program on the radio, inspiration might tell me to go to an event. I ask God why I need to be there and the only answer I get back is, "go to the event." Once there, incredible opportunities happen. I might meet a person whose services I need, or meet someone who connects me to a job because they saw me with my camera. It is always a wonderful experience. Listening to the Voice of Inspiration always delivers opportunities and introductions to people that I need to meet. When I'm at 100%, the Voice of Inspiration requests things of me that might seem unreasonable, however when I follow the request with **action**, miraculous things happen in my life. So part of my 100% is listening to and following up on the Voice of Inspiration with immediate action.

The Voice of Inspiration is connected to my Spirit, therefore the process of being 100% allows my Mind (Consciousness), Body (Instincts), and Spirit (Inspiration) to connect and not be separate. My 100% means wholeness, not fragmented separateness.

At 100%, I don't spend all of my time and energy satisfying bodily, primal, and instinctual needs. I give my body the essence of what it needs instead of temporary feel-good medicine, by keeping my body in line with the mind and spirit through exercise.

My body needs movement and to be exalted. It rules our domain. I remind my body to follow my spirit and consciousness by overriding its illusionary limitations. I push it beyond its capacity. When I do, a second wind or new energy takes over. Most people call this place the Zone. I love these moments of clarity when I'm no longer thinking about the moment, I am the moment.

At 100% I feel really connected to everything. At less than 100% my Mind and Spirit feel disconnected from my Body akin to an out-of body experience. When I have these feelings, my body does things that go beyond physical explanation—like Michael Jordan walking on air.

Alcohol, lust and other consumptions endeavor to keep me trapped by my bodily needs, separating my Body from my Spirit and Consciousness. At 100% I limit the temporary rush that feels good when I participate in these activities, otherwise the drug constantly needs to be fed. I remember that these forces are temporary, immediate and need constant recycling. I participate in activities that are everlasting and consistent, and control those that encourage the instant gratification to which we are all addicted.

I acknowledge and work to control the forces and trickery that keep me disconnected and unable to experience my 100%. I practice experiencing instant gratification through manifestation of thoughts, instead of the gratification that comes from consuming goods. At 100% I choose not to support a power structure whose only concern is taking our energy to maintain its position. The urge is there to witness our glory, our magnificence, and our 100%.

At 100%, I don't fanatically desire to witness and live vicariously through the accomplishments of others, or stand in judgment and get upset when they do something of which I don't approve. At 100%, I use the fan energy to focus and manifest accomplishments in my own life. At 100%, I take back the power I have given away to others.

MY 100 PERCENT STORY

JESSICA'S 100 PERCENT

I am 100% when my place is clean. It makes my whole day so much better! I don't wake up tripping over clothes, shoes and everything else on the floor. Waking up to a clean room just makes everything else easier! Waking up to clutter causes me confusion and automatic stress, and that's a horrible way to begin my day! Having a clean living area is a huge part of my life because I'm extremely busy with school, work and my non-profit, *Feeling Fabulous*. It feels amazing to come home to a clean house!

I am 100% when I attend church on the regular. Church contributes a great deal to the way I carry myself from day to day! After completing *30 Days at 100 Percent* I had to make some hard decisions to get my life back on track, and putting God first was one of them. I found that the weeks that I missed my Sunday "pick-me-up" service my *30 Days* percentage decreased from day to day. I was frustrated and irritated more often than normal. Once I started going to church every Sunday, I started to get Joy in my heart that is out of this world, and I now feel that opportunities with God are endless! I hope that he continues to use me to do his work!

I am 100% when I go to the gym at least 3-5 times a week. Now I have to be honest, at first it was soooo hard getting up to go to the gym every morning, but the feeling that I get afterwards is PRICELESS! Even if people can't see the weight loss, I Feel It and that's all that matters!

I am 100% when my hair, nails and makeup are done! After doing my first *30 Days*, I noticed that when I look 100% on the outside, it helps me feel 100% on the inside. When I know I look right, I hold my head up high and I put a little pep in my step because my confidence is out of this world! At first it was hard getting up every morning before work to put on my makeup and do my hair, but after the first week I got the hang of it! The confidence in return is priceless!

At 100% my place is clean, I'm at church every Sunday thanking God for his love and mercy, I'm at the gym to maintain my health, and my hair, nails and makeup are always on point!

I love myself and encourage women everywhere to feel the same way! After completing *30 Days at 100 Percent* I was extremely HAPPY AND LOVED MYSELF LIKE I'VE NEVER LOVED ME BEFORE! I feel like a queen inside and out! I wanted women all around the world to experience this feeling of self-worth that I feel every morning, so I started my own Foundation entitled " Feeling Fabulous"! Feeling Fabulous is a non-profit organization that teaches women how to" Unleash & Enhance the DIVA in them"! Needless to say at my 100%, I'm Feeling Fabulous!

Learn more about Jessica at ImFeelingFab.org. Where PINK isn't just a color, it's an attitude.

FOCUS

Several years ago, my good friend John Karubian, noticing how easily distracted I become, said to me, "Crystal if you will just put laser focus on your agency and books, you'll excel beyond your wildest dreams."

I never forgot it. Nonetheless, it has taken me at least five years, much prayer, and learning how to be still and meditate for me to arrive at this new place, doing this new thing. To be sure, I was a hot mess.

To most people on the outside looking in, I was successful. I owned a makeup, hair and styling agency, had self-published a book titled *The Hair Makeup & Fashion Styling Career Guide*, and was traveling around the country teaching master classes for MAC Cosmetics, as well as my own workshops. Every once in a while you might even get a glimpse of me on television.

But in private, and in the midst and aftermath of a terrible divorce, I had become easily distracted, quick to overwhelm, and had mastered the art of shuffling papers so it appeared as though I was getting something done.

Oh, I was busy, but being busy is not the same as being productive. Just like making money is not the same as creating wealth. I heard that a person without passion is easily distracted. I had clearly lost my passion. I knew something was terribly wrong when

over the phone one day I, Miss You-Can-Do-Anything, dissuaded a young person from trying something bold in order to get her product in front of a celebrity. Tough love, that's me. Discourage you—no. Something was wrong.

Somewhere along the way I had tired of being an agent. I knew it was time to go when calling on directors, producers, and photographers stopped being about art and relationship building, and started feeling like solicitation. It was time to pass the baton; but to whom, and then what? For 20 years I had gotten up every day excited to see what the new day would bring. And as passionate as I had been in 2001 to negotiate a $3,500 day rate for a hairstylist, in 2008, I couldn't care less.

All I knew was, that along the way I had found a love of writing, teaching and speaking to people about growing their businesses, while at the same time, I was doing a mediocre job of managing the agency that bore my name. Something had to give. What was needed was focus. But in order to focus, I had to have a NEW purpose driven life.

When I couldn't do it all on my own, God stepped in and gave me something bigger than myself to do. That thing was 30 DAYS AT 100 PERCENT.

For the first time in years, I focused as if my life

FOCUS

depended on it. As I acted out what I wrote in 30 DAYS, I got the clutter out of my life. I looked around, and took action to change the reasons that I couldn't think, or move beyond a snail's pace, or say no to things that were hurting me, or goodbye to people that I was allowing to waste my time. I figured out that I had given up and traded in my once fabulous purpose driven life for mediocrity and lack.

By the grace of God, and when I was ready for that bigger purpose, God gave me 30 DAYS AT 100 PERCENT as much to help me, as to help you. For over a year while I stressed about this and that, from time to time I would say what I knew; that I could change my entire life in 30 DAYS— All I had to do was focus. I guess the Big Guy said, "Well, let's see then."

Tom Alire, my sales manager at Xerox was fond of saying, "Better to aim high and miss, than to aim low and make it." I guess starting 30 DAYS on March 15th, and finishing it on May 26th is aiming high and missing it. What an awesome miss!

Inherent in the act of focusing is action. Nothing happens without it. My grandmother would often say, "Now you're cooking with gas." That's what action is, "cooking with gas." It's time for you to turn up the heat and make something happen.

To find out if 30 DAYS would really work, I distributed it to a few friends and colleagues. What I heard back astounded me. Fallon, a 20-something fashion stylist in Los Angeles found that when she made time to complete the next day's Action Plan before bed at night (*see page 112 for a sample, and 113 for an original that you can copy*) she could accomplish in three hours what had been taking her an entire day to do, opening the door for her to spend more time focusing on her career.

Quiana, a single mom in Philadelphia, incorporated the program into the lives of her two sons: Kobe, eight, and Mekhi, ten, and when everyone in the household was striving for 100%, she no longer had to struggle to get her two boys out of bed and ready for school in the morning. Sleeping in and fighting with Mommy was not their 100%.

Webster's Dictionary defines focus as a point of concentration, a center of activity, attraction or attention," a point at which rays converge and a thing is resolved into a clear image." Release the energy that you spend running around trying to solve a problem. Sit down and think of nothing else but the thing that needs your [focused] attention, and it will move.

In this first 30 days, focus your attention on identifying those things that keep you in bondage to a life half lived. Speak life into your 100%, and begin to move the rest out of your way, 30 days at a time!

MONTH 1: WEEK 1

30/**100**
PERCENT

MONTH, DAY - YEAR

MONDAY

....
....
....

....

%

TUESDAY

....
....
....

....

WEDNESDAY

....
....
....

....

WRITE
A
SHORT
THREE LINE
SYNOPSIS
(ABOUT THE
SAME AMOUNT
AS YOU WOULD
TWITTER,
FOR
EACH
DAY
AND
RECORD
YOUR
PERCENTAGE

THURSDAY

....
....
....

....

FRIDAY

....
....
....

....

SATURDAY

....
....
....

....

SUNDAY

....
....
....

....

SUB-TOTAL _____

DIVIDED BY 7 ÷ **7** =

THIS WEEK'S AVERAGE _____

How do you feel about week 1?

....

....

....

....

....

What could you have done differently?

....

....

....

....

....

What will you do differently next week?

....

....

....

....

....

Are you adding anything to week 2?   ___Yes   ___No
If yes, What?

....

....

....

If no, Why Not?

....

....

Other enlightening notes, thoughts
or observations about this week.
What worked and Why?
What didn't and Why Not?

_____

_____

_____

_____

_____

_____

_____

_____

_____

_____

Proverbs 4:25 - 27

I look straight ahead.
I stick to the path. I am safe.
I am not sidetracked.

FOCUS

CONFERENCE CALL 2 WEEK 1

NO CROSS TALK. NO FIXING OTHER PEOPLES' CHALLENGES. NO INTERRUPTIONS EXCEPT FOR A TIME STAMP. WHAT HAPPENS ON THE CALL STAYS ON THE CALL.

What's Working?

1) ....

2) ....

What's Not?

1) ....

2) ....

What successes have you had so far?

1) ....

2) ....

What challenges are you experiencing?

1) ....

2) ....

NOTES: ....

WORKIN' THE PLAN

NOTES

....
....
....
....
....
....
....
....
....
....
....
....
....
....
....
....
....
....
....
....
....
....
....
....
....
....
....
....
....

MONTH 1: WEEK 2

30/100 PERCENT

MONDAY

....
....
....

%

TUESDAY

....
....
....

....

WRITE
A
SHORT
SYNOPSIS
*(ABOUT THE SAME
AS YOU WOULD
TWITTER)*
FOR
EACH
DAY
AND
RECORD
YOUR
PERCENTAGE

WEDNESDAY

....
....
....

....

THURSDAY

....
....
....

....

FRIDAY

....
....
....

....

SATURDAY

....
....
....

....

SUNDAY

....
....
....

....

SUB-TOTAL _____

DIVIDED BY 7 ÷ **7** =

THIS WEEK'S AVERAGE _____

DO NOT FEEL COMPELLED TO ADD ANYTHING NEW UNTIL YOU HAVE MASTERED
THE THING YOU ARE DETERMINED TO ACCOMPLISH!

How do you feel about week 2?

....

....

....

....

....

What could you have done differently?

....

....

....

....

....

What will you do differently next week?

....

....

....

....

....

Are you adding anything to week 3?   ___Yes   ___No
If yes, What?

....

....

....

If no, Why Not?

....

....

....

Other enlightening notes, thoughts
or observations about this week.
What worked and Why?
What didn't and Why Not?

_____

_____

_____

_____

_____

_____

_____

_____

_____

_____

If you
stay ready,
you won't have to
get ready.

PREPARATION

30/100 PERCENT

CONFERENCE CALL 1 WEEK2

What's Working?

1) ....

....

....

....

2) ....

....

....

....

What's Not?

1) ....

....

....

....

2) ....

....

....

....

What successes have you had so far?

1) ....

....

....

....

2) ....

....

....

....

What challenges are you experiencing?

1) ....

....

....

....

2) ....

....

....

....

NOTES: ....

....

....

....

....

CONFERENCE CALL 2 WEEK2

NO CROSS TALK. NO FIXING OTHER PEOPLES' CHALLENGES. NO INTERRUPTIONS
EXCEPT FOR A TIME STAMP. WHAT HAPPENS ON THE CALL STAYS ON THE CALL.

What's Working?

1) ....

....

....

....

2) ....

....

....

....

What successes have you had so far?

1) ....

....

....

....

2) ....

....

....

....

What's Not?

1) ....

....

....

....

2) ....

....

....

....

What challenges are you experiencing?

1) ....

....

....

....

2) ....

....

....

....

NOTES: ....

....

....

....

....

MONTH 1: WEEK 3

MONTH, DAY - YEAR

%

MONDAY

....

....

....

TUESDAY

....

....

....

WEDNESDAY

....

....

....

THURSDAY

....

....

....

FRIDAY

....

....

....

SATURDAY

....

....

....

SUNDAY

....

....

....

WRITE
A
SHORT
THREE LINE
SYNOPSIS
*(ABOUT THE
SAME AMOUNT
AS YOU WOULD
TWITTER)*
FOR
EACH
DAY
AND
RECORD
YOUR
PERCENTAGE

SUB-TOTAL   _____

DIVIDED BY 7   ÷ **7** =

THIS WEEK'S AVERAGE   _____

DO NOT FEEL COMPELLED TO ADD ANYTHING NEW UNTIL YOU HAVE MASTERED
THE THING YOU ARE DETERMINED TO ACCOMPLISH!

How do you feel about week 3?

....

....

....

....

....

What could you have done differently?

....

....

....

....

....

What will you do differently next week?

....

....

....

....

....

Are you adding anything to week 4? ___Yes ___No
If yes, What?

....

....

....

If no, Why Not?

....

....

....

Other enlightening notes, thoughts
or observations about this week.
What worked and Why?
What didn't and Why Not?

_____

_____

_____

_____

_____

_____

_____

_____

> "When you write down your
> ideas you automatically
> focus your
> full attention on them.
> Few if any of us can write one
> thought and think another
> at the same time.
> Thus a pencil and paper make
> excellent concentration tools."
>
> —Michael Leboeuf

30/100 PERCENT

CONFERENCE CALL 1 WEEK3

NO CROSS TALK. NO FIXING OTHER PEOPLES' CHALLENGES. NO INTERRUPTIONS EXCEPT FOR A TIME STAMP. WHAT HAPPENS ON THE CALL STAYS ON THE CALL.

What's Working?

1) ....

....

....

....

2) ....

....

....

....

What successes have you had so far?

1) ....

....

....

....

2) ....

....

....

....

What's Not?

1) ....

....

....

....

2) ....

....

....

....

What challenges are you experiencing?

1) ....

....

....

....

2) ....

....

....

....

NOTES: ....

....

....

....

....

CONFERENCE CALL 2 WEEK3

NO CROSS TALK. NO FIXING OTHER PEOPLES' CHALLENGES. NO INTERRUPTIONS EXCEPT FOR A TIME STAMP. WHAT HAPPENS ON THE CALL STAYS ON THE CALL.

What's Working?

1) ....

....

....

....

2) ....

....

....

....

What successes have you had so far?

1) ....

....

....

....

2) ....

....

....

....

What's Not?

1) ....

....

....

....

2) ....

....

....

....

What challenges are you experiencing?

1) ....

....

....

....

2) ....

....

....

....

NOTES: ....

....

....

....

....

MONTH 1: WEEK 4

PERCENT

MONTH, DAY - YEAR

MONDAY
....
....
....

%

TUESDAY
....
....
....

....

WRITE
A
SHORT
THREE LINE
SYNOPSIS
*(ABOUT THE
SAME AMOUNT
AS YOU WOULD
TWITTER)*
FOR
EACH
DAY
AND
RECORD
YOUR
PERCENTAGE

WEDNESDAY
....
....
....

....

THURSDAY
....
....
....

....

FRIDAY
....
....
....

....

SATURDAY
....
....
....

....

SUNDAY
....
....
....

....

SUB-TOTAL _____

DIVIDED BY 7 ÷ **7** =

THIS WEEK'S AVERAGE _____

How do you feel about week 4?

....

....

....

....

....

Other enlightening notes, thoughts
or observations about this week.
What worked and Why?
What didn't and Why Not?

What could you have done differently?

....

....

....

....

....

What will you do differently next week?

....

....

....

....

....

Are you adding anything to week 5?   ___Yes   ___No
If yes, What?

....

....

....

If no, Why Not?

....

....

....

"Plan the Work,
and
Work the Plan."

—Tom Alire
My Sales Manager, Xerox
Seattle, WA

CONFERENCE CALL 1 WEEK4

NO CROSS TALK. NO FIXING OTHER PEOPLES' CHALLENGES. NO INTERRUPTION
EXCEPT FOR A TIME STAMP. WHAT HAPPENS ON THE CALL STAYS ON THE CALL

What's Working?

1) ....

2) ....

What's Not?

1) ....

2) ....

What successes have you had so far?

1) ....

2) ....

What challenges are you experiencing?

1) ....

2) ....

NOTES: ....

CONFERENCE CALL 2 WEEK4

NO CROSS TALK. NO FIXING OTHER PEOPLES' CHALLENGES. NO INTERRUPTIONS EXCEPT FOR A TIME STAMP. WHAT HAPPENS ON THE CALL STAYS ON THE CALL.

What's Working?

1) ....
....
....
....

2) ....
....
....
....

What's Not?

1) ....
....
....
....

2) ....
....
....
....

What successes have you had so far?

1) ....
....
....
....

2) ....
....
....
....

What challenges are you experiencing?

1) ....
....
....
....

2) ....
....
....
....

NOTES: ....
....
....
....
....

MONTH 1: EXTRA DAYS

MONTH, DAY - YEAR

%

MONDAY

....

....

....

TUESDAY

....

....

....

WEDNESDAY

....

....

....

THURSDAY

....

....

....

FRIDAY

....

....

....

SATURDAY

....

....

....

SUNDAY

....

....

....

WRITE A SHORT THREE LINE SYNOPSIS *(ABOUT THE SAME AMOUNT AS YOU WOULD TWITTER)* FOR EACH DAY AND RECORD YOUR PERCENTAGE

SUB-TOTAL _____

DIVIDED BY THE # OF DAYS IN **THIS** WEEK

÷ __ =

THIS WEEK'S AVERAGE _____

NOTES

....
....
....
....
....
....
....
....
....
....
....
....
....
....
....
....
....
....
....
....
....

....
....
....
....
....
....
....
....
....
....
....
....
....
....
....
....

THE STORY YOU TELL

Excuses are the building blocks to nothing, those that excel in them, seldom excel at anything else.

RATIONALIZATION

MONTH 1 _____

WEEK 1

....
....
....
....

WEEK 2

WRITE
A
SHORT
THREE LINE
SYNOPSIS
(ABOUT THE
SAME AMOUNT
AS YOU WOULD
TWITTER)
FOR
EACH
DAY
AND
RECORD
YOUR
PERCENTAGE

....
....
....
....

WEEK 3

....
....
....
....

WEEK 4

....
....
....
....

WEEK 5

....
....
....

SUB-TOTAL _____

DIVIDED BY 5 $\div$ **5** =

THIS MONTHS AVERAGE _____

NOTES

....
....
....
....
....
....
....
....
....
....
....
....
....
....
....
....
....
....
....
....

....
....
....
....
....
....
....
....
....
....
....
....
....
....
....

ROMANS 12:2

I am
transformed
by the renewing
of my mind.

CHANGE YOUR THINKING

PERCENT

MONTH 1 MY TRIUMPHS

Other enlightening notes, thoughts or observations about this week. What worked and Why? What didn't and Why Not?

....

....

....

....

....

....

....

....

....

....

....

....

....

....

....

....

....

....

....

_____

_____

_____

_____

_____

_____

_____

_____

> "It's who you become,
> as you overcome the obstacles
> necessary to achieve your
> goals, that can give you the
> deepest and most
> long-lasting sense of
> fulfillment."
>
> —Anthony Robbins
>
> **VISION**

MOMENTUM

Y ou're still with me. Now that's what I'm talking about! Through Momentum we gain strength and force, a by-product of forward motion. Momentum is about gain.

In the Momentum phase of 30 DAYS AT 100 PERCENT we take advantage of our forward motion, and we don't let up.

Halfway through Momentum, you will notice that new ideas begin to emerge through the clarity that you experience in the space where mental, physical or emotional clutter used to reside. You begin to contemplate plans for bigger and better things in your life. New ways of doing things emerge.

The idea of beginning or completing a project of some significance begins to take hold, and you start believing your Source for more. The idea of taking a class, starting a business, getting involved in a group, writing a book, committing some of your time to a worthwhile cause, or changing careers begins to take root. The mind that at one time, couldn't see how to squeeze another thing into your day, now finds it possible to make room for and excel at something new.

Having made it to Momentum, you live in the Now, and start making choices that impact your future positively.

It is Here and Now that you win the battle for your mind to stay focused on the goal that yields the greatest gain in each area of your life.

Now as you revisit your AREAS OF OPPORTUNITY to determine if you would like to add or hold, you look toward adding those things that will benefit you in the long term, but keep you focused today.

Don't overdo it. As you may remember from my weight loss days I only added one, sometimes two things each month. That's because **I know me**, and if I take on too much before I've mastered the new thing I'm working on, I become overwhelmed, and very frustrated.

As the goat of the zodiac, it's my way to be steady and methodical, always gaining ground, but slow and sure. I encourage you to give yourself time to grow into this new life you're creating.

Momentum is also the silver lining phase where you can experience unexpected growth in a particular area, and some wonderful "ah-ha" moments of remembering how good it feels to be on top of your game.

For me, those "ah-ha"moments came in the

MOMENTUM

consistency of mastering my outward appearance—perfecting my morning beauty routine of doing my brows, lashes, cheeks, and lips, and styling hair every single day for fifty-one straight days [and counting].

Momentum is the place where the finish line starts to come into view.

....

....

....

....

....

....

....

....

....

....

....

....

....

....

....

....

....

....

....

....

....

....

....

....

....

....

....

....

....

....

....

....

....

....

MONTH 2: WEEK 1

30/100
PERCENT

%

MONTH, DAY - YEAR

MONDAY

....

....

....

TUESDAY

....

....

....

WEDNESDAY

....

....

....

THURSDAY

....

....

....

FRIDAY

....

....

....

SATURDAY

....

....

....

SUNDAY

....

....

....

WRITE
A
SHORT
THREE LINE
SYNOPSIS
(ABOUT THE
SAME AMOUNT
AS YOU WOULD
TWITTER)
FOR
EACH
DAY
AND
RECORD
YOUR
PERCENTAGE

SUB-TOTAL   _____

DIVIDED BY 7   ÷ **7** =

THIS WEEK'S AVERAGE   _____

How do you feel about week 5?

....

....

....

....

....

What could you have done differently?

....

....

....

....

....

What will you do differently next week?

....

....

....

....

....

Are you adding anything to week 6?   ___Yes   ___No
If yes, What?

....

....

....

If no, Why Not?

....

....

....

Other enlightening notes, thoughts
or observations about this week.
What worked and Why?
What didn't and Why Not?

_____

_____

_____

_____

_____

_____

_____

_____

_____

_____

_____

_____

"Failure to act is often the
greatest failure of all."
—UCLA Bruins
Coach John Wooden

ACTION

MONTH 2: WEEK 2

30/100 PERCENT

MONTH, DAY - YEAR

%

MONDAY

....

....

....

TUESDAY

....

....

....

WEDNESDAY

....

....

....

THURSDAY

....

....

....

FRIDAY

....

....

....

SATURDAY

....

....

....

SUNDAY

....

....

....

WRITE
A
SHORT
SYNOPSIS
*(ABOUT THE SAME
AS YOU WOULD
TWITTER)*
FOR
EACH
DAY
AND
RECORD
YOUR
PERCENTAGE

SUB-TOTAL _____

DIVIDED BY 7   ÷ **7** =

THIS WEEK'S AVERAGE _____

DO NOT FEEL COMPELLED TO ADD ANYTHING NEW UNTIL YOU HAVE MASTERED
THE THING YOU ARE DETERMINED TO ACCOMPLISH!

How do you feel about week 6?

....
....
....
....
....

What could you have done differently?

....
....
....
....
....

What will you do differently next week?

....
....
....
....
....

Are you adding anything to week 7? ___Yes ___No
If yes, What?

....
....
....

If no, Why Not?

....
....
....

Other enlightening notes, thoughts
or observations about this week.
What worked and Why?
What didn't and Why Not?

_____

_____

_____

_____

_____

_____

_____

_____

_____

ECCLESIASTES 5:12

Fill your day with good
wholesome activities.
Exert your best efforts in the
work of the day.

MOVE

MONTH 2: WEEK 3

30/100 PERCENT

MONTH, DAY - YEAR

MONDAY

....
....
....

%

....

TUESDAY

....
....
....

....

WRITE
A
SHORT
THREE LINE
SYNOPSIS
(ABOUT THE
SAME AMOUNT
AS YOU WOULD
TWITTER)
FOR
EACH
DAY
AND
RECORD
YOUR
PERCENTAGE

WEDNESDAY

....
....
....

....

THURSDAY

....
....
....

....

FRIDAY

....
....
....

....

SATURDAY

....
....
....

....

SUNDAY

....
....
....

....

SUB-TOTAL _____

DIVIDED BY 7 ÷ **7** =

THIS WEEK'S AVERAGE _____

DO NOT FEEL COMPELLED TO ADD ANYTHING NEW UNTIL YOU HAVE MASTERED
THE THING YOU ARE DETERMINED TO ACCOMPLISH!

How do you feel about week 7?

....
....
....
....
....

What could you have done differently?

....
....
....
....
....

What will you do differently next week?

....
....
....
....
....

Are you adding anything to week 8?   ___Yes ___No
If yes, What?

....
....
....

If no, Why Not?

....
....

Other enlightening notes, thoughts
or observations about this week.
What worked and Why?
What didn't and Why Not?

_____

_____

_____

_____

_____

_____

_____

_____

_____

_____

"If your position is
everywhere,
your momentum is zero."

—William N. Lipscomb

FOCUS

MONTH 2: WEEK 4

MONTH, DAY - YEAR

MONDAY

....

....

....   %

TUESDAY

....

....

WEDNESDAY

....

....

THURSDAY

....

....

FRIDAY

....

....

....

SATURDAY

....

....

SUNDAY

....

....

....

WRITE A SHORT THREE LINE SYNOPSIS *(ABOUT THE SAME AMOUNT AS YOU WOULD TWITTER)* FOR EACH DAY AND RECORD YOUR PERCENTAGE

SUB-TOTAL   _____

DIVIDED BY 7   ÷ 7 =

THIS WEEK'S AVERAGE   _____

How do you feel about week 8?

....
....
....
....
....

What could you have done differently?

....
....
....
....
....

What will you do differently next week?

....
....
....
....
....

Are you adding anything to week 9?   ___Yes   ___No
If yes, What?

....
....
....

If no, Why Not?

....
....

Other enlightening notes, thoughts
or observations about this week.
What worked and Why?
What didn't and Why Not?

_____
_____
_____
_____
_____
_____
_____
_____
_____

PROVERBS 6:11

Too much sleep brings
poverty. It is like a robber
who steals from you and
makes you helpless.

WAKE UP

MONTH 2: EXTRA DAYS

30/₁₀₀
PERCENT

%

MONDAY

....

....

....

TUESDAY

....

....

WEDNESDAY

....

....

THURSDAY

....

....

FRIDAY

....

....

SATURDAY

....

....

SUNDAY

....

....

....

....

....

....

....

....

....

WRITE
A
SHORT
THREE LINE
SYNOPSIS
*(ABOUT THE
SAME AMOUNT
AS YOU WOULD
TWITTER)*
FOR
EACH
DAY
AND
RECORD
YOUR
PERCENTAGE

SUB-TOTAL _____

DIVIDED BY 7 ÷ **7** =

THIS WEEK'S AVERAGE _____

NOTES

··

··

··

··

··

··

··

··

··

··

··

··

··

··

··

··

··

··

··

··

"To create **momentum** in your life, never leave the scene of a **decision** without taking action."

The action has to be:
1) in support of your decision no matter how insignificant, and
2) the action has to be something you're willing to do right **NOW**.

MONTH 2 _____

30/100 PERCENT

WEEK 1

....

....

....

....

WRITE
A
SHORT
THREE LINE
SYNOPSIS
*(ABOUT THE
SAME AMOUNT
AS YOU WOULD
TWITTER)*
FOR
EACH
DAY
AND
RECORD
YOUR
PERCENTAGE

WEEK 2

....

....

....

....

WEEK 3

....

....

....

....

WEEK 4

....

....

....

....

EXTRA DAYS

....

....

....

SUB-TOTAL   _____

DIVIDED BY 4   ÷ **4** =

THIS MONTHS AVERAGE   _____

NOTES

Other enlightening notes, thoughts
or observations about this week.
What worked and Why?
What didn't and Why Not?

"If you're coasting,
you're either losing
momentum
or you're headed
downhill."

— Joan Welsh

....
....
....
....
....
....
....
....
....
....
....
....
....
....
....
....
....
....
....
....

MONTH 2 MY TRIUMPHS

> "Never confuse motion
> with action."
>
> —Benjamin Franklin

DO SOMETHING

ACHIEVEMENT

In order for me to complete 30 DAYS AT 100 PERCENT, I had to get reacquainted with what I remembered about achieving in my own life. After writing the first 23 pages in a week and a half, I got stuck! Really stuck. I sat down to write and nothing came out. For 10 more days, nothing came out. And so, just as you have chosen me to be your coach in 30 DAYS AT 100 PERCENT, I turned to my coach, Tony Robbins. Yes! Sometimes I need help getting motivated too.

I grabbed Tony Robbins' "*Get The Edge*" CDs that had arrived a couple of weeks earlier, popped a couple of them into the CD player in my car, and began to listen. When I listen to Tony talk about why we underachieve, or how we get into a rut and allow mediocrity to take hold at different times in our lives, I realize that even people like Oprah are human and don't get through life without personal challenges. At least I know I'm in good company!

I kept saying to myself, "What do I tell them about achievement?" It had been several years since I had achieved anything sizable. Just gettin' up and doin' it, doin' it, doin' it every day, is not achieving. It's surviving. It's maintaining the status quo, but it is not achieving.

Inherent in achieving is purpose. But as I listened to Tony Robbins in my car, over and over again, I recalled how I had committed myself to writing the 'Career Guide' in my late 30s, anchored the 440 relay in my teens, and started Crystal Agency after leaving my job at Xerox, only to be unceremoniously fired by the photographer I quit my corporate job for in my 20s. "Surely if I just focus," I thought, "I could get this done!"

I began to take the advice I give the students who take my portfolio building workshops: "Figure out where you want to be in five years, three years, and one year, and work backwards from the goal." Make a decision to focus on the results that you want. Webster's dictionary defines an achievement as a result gained by the conscious exertion of your own power—an effort. A serious attempt.

It seems too simple, doesn't it? But let me show you. If you take the time to create a personal statement for yourself, then you are setting the wheels of the universe in motion by speaking your expectation into existence. It might sound like this: "On June 1, 2012 I will be working as an attorney for Jones, Bradford & Kelly Law Firm in Los Angeles, California making a starting salary of $150K a year." Write it down, and you become accountable to yourself. Now, take an action every single day. There is always plenty to do when you set out to accomplish something, but taking an action is what sepa-

ACHIEVEMENT

rates the men from the boys, so to speak.

If you choose taking home a big phat salary from a large prestigious law firm as your career goal, then there are certain things that will be required of you. For instance, in addition to getting great grades, you may have to choose a great school, which may take you out of your neighborhood, and your comfort zone; you will also need to master the art of networking, maybe even get an internship each summer.

Isn't it true that through research you can find out what law schools most of the partners in a law firm graduated from, and thus choose which law schools that you should apply to—to give yourself the best possible opportunity to get hired by that firm? Isn't it true that knowing that they only hire people who graduated at the top of their class will keep you from making a choice to stay out all night drinking before an important midterm when your GPA is at stake? Isn't it true that learning that all the partners at the firm committed a certain amount of their personal time to community service gives you a leg up, and a chance to add that same kind of service to your résumé?

That's what I mean. The choice of focusing on the outcome of becoming a member of the firm will cause you to make different choices for your life so that you can step into your destiny in three years. That is Achievement! And every step along the way, every bit of the research to find out about the firm, are the actions that you must take on your journey to Achievement.

Coincidentally, I recently spoke with a makeup artist who had taken one of my classes in 2008. We'll call her Alice. She wanted me to take a look at her online image portfolio, which I did and thought was just beautiful. Then she said "But I'm not getting any work." Now for those of you who don't know, I teach a day-long portfolio building and marketing workshop for makeup, hair and fashion stylists that teaches them how to create résumés, promotional cards, an online presence, as well as how to negotiate, and find an agency to represent them.

When I asked her what she had done since class to promote herself, she said "I contacted magazines." "Okay, and how many magazines did you contact?" I asked. "One," she said. I won't even repeat exactly what I said to her when she revealed that little tidbit.

She went on to tell me that she had contacted Allure magazine, once, by sending a link to the editor. She had also followed up, one time, by making a phone call. That was at least six months before, and she had not followed up since. "Is that what I

ACHIEVEMENT

told you to do?" I asked her. "Alice" I said, "one phone call is not even an effort." Unfortunately, Alice is not alone. As I travel around the country teaching freelance artists how to make themselves stand out in a crowded marketplace, at some point in the conversation about how to get more work, we always discuss outgoing phone calls to creative decision-makers, which is active and places you on the offense.

Whenever my students start recounting their stories of defeat after giving up on calling a potential client, I am compelled to ask the question, "Well, how many times did you follow-up?" Inevitably, 80-90 percent of the class responds, "Once or twice." Once or twice, I tell them, is not an effort. In truth, if you are going to give up after two phone calls, you wasted your time making the calls at all. People who strive to live at 100% would never give up after two phone calls.

In advertising, the rule of thumb is that in order to get a consumer to switch from one brand to another, an advertiser must bombard the consumer with messages at least nine times. We get those messages everywhere don't we? On television, on billboards, in magazines, in email, even while you wait on hold? That's five times right there. I tell my students they don't have permission to give up on a prospect until they have connected with that person at least nine times. Nine times is

at least an effort!

Focus on results, not the process. If the result you want is to make more money, you will have to DO SOMETHING! You will have to actively pursue that which you say you want because, quite frankly, everything else is lip service.

Tony Robbins blew me away the other day in the car when, while listening to his tape, I heard him say, "People who do nothing, focus on the process." I call that the minutia. The itty, bitty details that you can delegate to someone else. Focus on the *outcome*—the big picture.

Robbins recounted a story told by the winningest college basketball coach in US history, former UCLA Bruin head coach John Wooden, who said to his players "If you don't give 100% only you will know, but that still makes you a loser because you only get to keep that which you give away." I think that is so deep. If you give 100% you get to keep the results.

As I wrote 30 DAYS AT 100 PERCENT, I had moments when I started thinking about those itty bitty things, like how was I going to get it printed, where was the money going to come from, what if no one liked it, what if everyone liked it. Stop the madness! I kept hearing God's

ACHIEVEMENT

voice telling me, "Just finish it—I got this!"

Letting go of old bad habits is hard to do. But I had to keep reminding myself about the other successes that I have had in my life. Hellooo? I had already written *The Hair Makeup & Fashion Styling Career Guide*. I wrote it. I got it printed, and they delivered 2000 of them to my home, and I put them in my garage on two pallets. My poor husband Michael couldn't even park his Range Rover in the garage for months.

I don't remember a single detail of how those books got from my computer into my garage, but when I didn't know how to write a book, I went to a bookstore and sat down in the self-help aisle and looked for books on, guess what––how to write a book. Surprisingly, there are thousands of people who have done it before and who were more than happy to share their knowledge with me for $15.95.

Focus on the reward, the outcome, the end product, and then raise your expectations—that which you believe you deserve.

Now is the time to take advantage of the focus and Momentum that have manifested in you these last 60 days. With them comes the desire to do a new thing and take on a new challenge. That new thing is a Goal.

Choose to do a NEW thing regardless of your circumstances. Those circumstances are just a detail. Look at your situation and believe that the experience and knowledge that you gathered from the 10 years that you worked for a company that then fired you makes you ripe to open your own consulting firm. Believe it, take action, and the details will work themselves out.

Believe that just as Sylvia Rhone became the first African-American woman to make it into the boys club that is the music industry when she became the "CEO" in Elektra Entertainment, the "E" in WEA, Warner, Elektra, Atlantic, that you, too, can rise to become the CEO of a Fortune 500 company.

Believe as Steve Jobs did five years ago when everyone wrote Apple off, and I couldn't even buy the latest edition of QuickBooks for my Macintosh computer, that Apple would one day rule and everyone would own an iPod.

Believe in the vision you once had of your marriage as perfect, and focus on the actions that you must take to create that future NOW.

Believe, as you look at a situation that needs fixing and shake your head wondering who is going to take charge, that YOU are the answer, and have the capacity and the God-given talent to make a

ACHIEVEMENT

difference, because you are more than a conqueror!

Believe in your ability to find the perfect mate, and then raise the expectations you have of yourself to become the kind of mate that you would want to partner with.

Believe as Barack Obama did, when people began to write him off when he was down 30% in the polls, and at one point no one even knew who he was, that he could rise to lead the most powerful country in the world.

Achievement demands that a clear, concise, quantifiable target be identified. If you don't know where you are going, how will you know when you have arrived?

Even the city of Los Angeles has freeway signs that let you know that you are approaching the city, how many miles before you arrive, and how many exits remain before you leave the city limits.

Achievement occurs when you consciously exert your own power onto the target. That power is called Effort, the act of making a serious attempt. Achievement takes focused Effort. A to-do list is not good enough. I ball those up and throw them away every day, and so do you!

To experience Achievement you must first create the target that you are aiming for—the bull's-eye, the Goal. Of course, you must write it down. I want it staring you in the face every single day. (By the way, when you need something in your face, try a dry erase marker on the bathroom mirror. That works for me!)

Next, you must have a Purpose, the *why* you want to do or have a thing.

Lastly, you must have a great big measurable Payoff that you are going to realize as a result of taking actions to achieve this new thing, this Goal.

If you set a goal to go back to college to get your bachelor degree, then it's crucial that your Goal contain elements that can be measured.

Who will you be with that degree? What will you gain, where will you work, why is the degree important to you, when will you graduate, how will your life be positively impacted by the attainment of this goal? How much money will you earn?

Then there is Action. Nothing happens without it. Actionable items, the completion of which keep you motivated and energized, propel you forward toward achieving the goal.

100 PERCENT

ACHIEVEMENT

CHOOSE NOT TO BE COMMON

I choose not to be a common [wo]man

It's my right to be uncommon if I can.

I seek opportunity, not security.

I do not wish to be a kept citizen,

humbled and dulled by having the State look after me.

I want to take the calculated risk,

to dream and to build,

to fail, and to succeed.

I refuse to live from hand to mouth.

I prefer the challenges of life to a guaranteed existence,

the thrill of fulfillment to the stale calm of utopia.

I will not trade freedom for charity,

nor my dignity for a handout.

I will not cower before any master, nor bend to any threat.

It is my heritage to stand erect, proud and unafraid,

to face the world boldly and say,

'This, I have done.'

Written by Dean Alfange,
American Statesman between 1942 and 1950
As I heard it [slightly altered] by Motivational Speaker Les Brown

30 DAYS
100 PERCENT

GOALS

Being 100% demands that you put laser-like Focus on, Momentum to, and Action behind a Goal, and then push. Push through the imaginary limitations, contrived constraints, and excuses about lack of time. Demand that your distractions take a back seat to your now and your future. Give power to possibility by staying focused on the outcome.

Goals give you purpose and clarity in a busy and hectic world. They act as a great homing device, always bringing you back to your purpose, the road map that keeps you focused on where you are going. Working toward an important goal adds value to your life, and achieving it will often lead you to your bigger life purpose.

The first step to achieving a Goal, is to write it down so that it becomes tangible, and real. A Goal that is never committed to paper is easily dismissed, because you never truly have to face it. Without a date from which you can work backwards, the Goal soon becomes something you were 'thinking about doing, at some time later on'—you know, just as soon as you get some time. The second, third, and forth steps are Action, Action, Action. Without doing something NOW, creating that forward motion, a dream never becomes a reality.

On pages 84 and 85 you will see an example of my thought process, and the list of actions that I took when I started writing *The Hair Makeup & Fashion Styling Career Guide*. Study it, and then turn to pages 86 and 87 to begin formulating the plan for achieving your own Goal.

What about all those people who will tell you that you can't? Well, that's not news; people will always tell you that you can't do something they don't believe that *they* can do. Isn't that how they have been keeping you from striving for 100% all these years? Isn't that why you didn't do this sooner? Don't you already know their names? If you want to achieve a goal, keep it to yourself. Stop giving other people the power to steal your dreams.

Most of us have had, or have those people in our lives. I quit my job at Xerox to represent a photographer who fired me six months later. I was devastated, but not devastated enough not to call my grandmother and tell her that the first child in our family to go to college had not only dropped out, but now had been fired by the photographer she quit her Fortune 500 job to work for. When I told my boyfriend I was going to start my own business

GOALS

he said, "You can't do that, you didn't even graduate from college." I might have been without a job, but I was still **Frances Wilkinson's grandchild**, and as I reminded him, "I can DO whatever I set my mind to."

He was not unique in his skepticism, nor are those other people in your life who dare you to step out on faith and try something at which they have already failed, or never had the nerve to try. The next time someone says, "Who do you think you are?" tell them you are **Frances Wilkinson's grandchild**.

In my life there was always my grandmother, "Gaga." Aunt Babe, as she was known to my friends, family and beaus, who, always seemed to like her better than they did me. Who, in spite of the fact that we actually had no money to speak of, had convinced me that I was going to college. Furthermore, I believed that I was living a life of privilege in spite of the fact that my grandfather had gambled away the family fortune before I was born, thereby denying me an opportunity to go to Annie Wright Academy—the oldest private boarding school in the West.

It wasn't until I had finally decided on Seattle University and presented the cost ($180 per credit hour at the time) to my grandmother that she said "Well, you had better get a job." Mortified, I said, "Job? I'm going to college. Why on earth would I get a job? Haven't you all been saving money all these years for my education?" My grandmother looked at me like I was nuts. She just shook her head and said "Crystal, we are poor. I have been telling you that for years." I just didn't believe it!

From the time I was about five years old, my grandmother said to me, "You, are going to college." This, even though not a single person in my family had ever gone, nor did anyone know how to get me there. Still, it was a defacto truth. I was going to college.

When I left my mom's house and moved into my grandmother's house at five years old, she told me I only had to do three things to live with her: go to school, get good grades and play sports. "You go to school" she said, "to get an education. You get good grades so that you can go to any college you want to, and you play sports so that you are competitive. That way when you grow up, you can take care of yourself." She planted the seed, and I managed myself to those four goals. Education. Good grades. Sports. College.

GOALS

When I didn't have a Goal, she set one for me. The purpose of those Goals was to create a well-educated, self-sufficient, poised young woman with a commitment to excellence, one who would have the wherewithal to sustain herself, the drive and determination to face life's curve balls, possess the ability to think on her feet and the desire to rise above her circumstances.

In 1975 when I went to see my college counselor with my 3.2 GPA—a solid B average—and told him that I was going to college, he told me pointedly. "You are not qualified to go to a four year university. You would be better off in a vocational technical school." (It was a different time. That's what they told all of us black kids back then).

Now imagine how that might have affected me had I not been lead ALL of my life toward the goal of a higher education through college. As far as I was concerned, it was my birthright. We have all seen what happens to children and adults who live without purpose. Even those of us with goals can get off track. Hellooo?

But as I sat in that man's office, and he repeated that nonsense to me, I picked my books up off of the floor, stood up from the chair I was sitting in,

and turned to walk out the door. When he realized I was leaving he said, "Where are you going?" I told him "My grandmother said I'm going to college" and I walked out of that little room where he kept his little brain, his small ideas, and his sad prejudices that the rest of the world was abandoning every day. And that was that! My best friend Janice's mom was a teacher, and she knew what to do, so my grandmother relied on her to help her fulfill the purpose that she had for my life. Pretty soon there were college catalogs and applications everywhere, and we were on our way.

There was no need to yell, scream or throw things when I could just get up and walk right out of that counselor's office. Ahh, the power of saying little and moving much!

This entire process of 30 DAYS AT 100 PERCENT is about you designing a new life for yourself. Living life at 100% takes work until you have replaced all the bad habits with a new routine. Inherent in this new routine is a commitment to excellence. You are choosing not to be common. You can be an extraordinary president, manager, entrepreneur, mother, student, athlete, parent, spouse, coach, assis-

GOALS

tant, teacher, or employee. But it takes a decision. Everything in life is a choice! **Choose**.

I attend Faithful Central Bible Church in Inglewood, California. One Sunday morning Bishop Ulmer said, "Stop telling God how big your problems are, and start telling your problems how big your God is!" You can do the same with your goals. Don't try to figure out the "how" yet. How is just a detail. Focus on the big "Thing" that needs to be created, envisioned, built or planned.

If your marriage is falling apart because you are cheating on your spouse, make a decision to stop it, right now. Set a Goal to be faithful and then write down the actions that you will take to make it happen:

1) Call that other person, say goodbye and STOP the madness.
2) Come home after work.
3) Set a date night with your spouse.
4) Get some counseling, and so on.

If the students in your 6th grade class are not going to be able to get jobs in a competitive workplace because they can't speak proper English, make a decision to improve their futures in nine months by implementing new teaching methods. Set a goal to raise their expectations and their reading level and write down the actions that you will take to make it happen:

1) Write down 10 reasons why you became a teacher in the first place.
2) Decide to correct their English every time they speak incorrectly regardless of how tedious it is.
3) Seek out and take a class with innovative teaching methods, and so on.

If you keep getting passed over for promotion at your job because you didn't finish your bachelor's degree, either become an entrepreneur or stop trying to reinvent the wheel and make a decision to go back to school now. Set a Goal to complete your degree in two years and then write down the actions that you will commit to, to make it happen:

1) Contact Human Resources to see if they will pay for you to go back to school.
2) Research 10 online schools that offer the classes you need to take to complete your degree.

GOALS

3) Find out if any of your current work experience can be counted as credits toward your degree.

4) If your job won't pay for school, decide how much money you will save from each paycheck and how long it will take before you can register for your first class.

5) Find out if the school you want to attend offers scholarships, and/or financial aid.

6) Request the financial aid and/or scholarship applications, and so on.

No more excuses. This is real life. All the silver spoons have been handed out. You didn't get one, and neither did I.

I have always believed that there was a God. I was raised in a small African Methodist Episcopal church in Tacoma, Washington, and I loved everything about it. It was conservative—we had to beg my grandmother, who was the choir director, to let us clap when we learned the new song "Oh Happy Day," but after that, they couldn't stop us.

But Allen AME church was the best. As kids, we sang in the choir, were members of the Usher Board, participated in the youth group, helped out with events whenever we could, served and looked out for the old folks and just generally were blessed to be raised by an entire community of people who loved us.

But as I look back, other than memorizing all of the books of the Bible, there was no discussion about what it meant to pray in such a way that you could actually activate the power of God in your life. As an adult who makes time to read and study God's word, I AM learning to "Let Go, and Let God." I create, and the HOW anything is going to get done, isn't my domain.

Instead of wondering how I'm going to distribute a product that I haven't even completed, I focus on the creation and completion of the product. Beyond that, I refuse to worry about it. I grab an 8-1/2 X 11 inch sheet of paper, and I write on it exactly the thing that I have no idea how to get done. I stand in the middle of my floor, and drop it metaphorically at God's feet knowing that over the weeks or months that I work to complete my part of the project, everything else will be revealed to me as I need it. People will be placed in my path,

GOALS

doors will open, opportunities will present themselves, and I will tackle each one as it comes, creating new goals along the way.

Why should I worry about where the money is going to come from to print 30 DAYS before it is even finished? I didn't even know how many pages it would be. To focus on how much money I need to print could easily overwhelm me and keep me from doing the most important thing, Finish the Book! Focus on the *goal*, not the *process*.

Now, to my own action list I add:

1) Needing to estimate the price of printing the book is a good thing.

2) Going to a bookstore to identify the competition is a good thing.

3) Learning how authors market their books is a good thing.

4) Looking up literary agents and determining which ones offer deals to authors who write in the self-help genre is a good thing.

All of these are great action items, and they become part of the plan, but I do not let them become more important than the Goal, because without a book, I don't need an agent, or printing estimates.

So look at my example on pages 84 and 85, and then go for it on pages 86 and 87. This book has space for three Goals; however, I really want you to focus on just one in the next 30 days. Remember, you are still working to maintain 100% in other areas of your life.

It may take you a few days to flesh everything out in this first Goal; especially the action items which typically continue to come to you day after day. In my own experience, I can usually write down 5-10 actions the first time that I sit down to focus on the Goal. Later, as the days go by, I find new actions popping into my head that, prior to creating the book, I would write down on napkins that I shoved into my purse, or send voice mail messages to myself, to retrieve later.

Hopefully now you will keep your 30 DAYS AT 100 PERCENT workbook with you in a briefcase, purse, or computer bag so that you can quickly and easily log important actions, thoughts, accomplishments and revelations as they come to you.

30/100 PERCENT

GOAL 1: *Write Hair Makeup*

DATE CREATED: <u>02/16/94</u>

DEFINE

GOAL ▸ Write a 16-page manual that will guide aspiring makeup, hair and fashion stylists in building their portfolios so they can get representation.

PURPOSE ▸ Help aspiring artists create representation worthy presentations that include their portfolios, comp cards, resumés and business cards that showcase their work properly.

PAYOFF ▸ To establish Crystal Agency as the defacto expert on career building for the freelance makeup, hair and fashion stylist. Get people to take us more seriously.

#	ACTIONS I WILL TAKE TO ACHIEVE MY GOAL	DATE COMPL'D
	Visit bookstore - locate books on how to write a book	2/19
	Write an outline	
	Get an ISBN Number	
	Find out how to create a barcode	
	Estimate the cost of printing	
	Call UCLA. Request course catalog - register 4 writing course	2/17
	Find a cover photo	
	Approach advertisers	
	Find an editor	
	Identify 2 people from each discipline to interview (Music,	
	Fashion, Editorial, Movies, Videos and TV)	2/29

EXPAND THE VISION

ACHIEVE DATE: 02/15/95

Who: *The authority on all things related to establishing a successful career as a freelance makeup, hair or fashion stylist.*

What: *Credibility in the fashion, beauty & entertainment. Become the go-to girl for career advice first pick of higher caliber talent.*

When: *1 Year. On February 15, 1995 I will send this book to the printer.*

Why: *Because the makeup schools aren't preparing students for work, or teaching them what their portfolios should look like to get work in print, video, film or TV.*

How: *I will make $60,000. on 2,000 books @ $40 ea., after expenses.*

◄ **WHO**
will I be

◄ **WHAT**
will I Gain

◄ **WHEN**
will it Happen

◄ **WHY**
is it Important

◄ **HOW**
will I Benefit

#	MORE ACTIONS I WILL TAKE TO ACHIEVE MY GOAL	DATE COMPL'D
___	_____	___
___	_____	___
___	_____	___
___	_____	___
___	_____	___
___	_____	___
___	_____	___
___	_____	___
___	_____	___
___	_____	___

30/100 PERCENT

GOAL 1: _____

DATE CREATED: _____

DEFINE

GOAL ▸ _____

PURPOSE ▸ _____

PAYOFF ▸ _____

#	ACTIONS I WILL TAKE TO ACHIEVE MY GOAL	DATE COMPL'D
___	_____	_____
___	_____	_____
___	_____	_____
___	_____	_____
___	_____	_____
___	_____	_____
___	_____	_____
___	_____	_____
___	_____	_____
___	_____	_____
___	_____	_____

_____

EXPAND THE VISION

ACHIEVE DATE: _____

_____

_____

_____

_____

_____

_____

_____

_____

_____

◄ **WHO**
will I be

◄ **WHAT**
will I Gain

◄ **WHEN**
will it Happen

◄ **WHY**
is it Important

◄ **HOW**
will I Benefit

#	MORE ACTIONS I WILL TAKE TO ACHIEVE MY GOAL	DATE COMPL'D
___	_____	___
___	_____	___
___	_____	___
___	_____	___
___	_____	___
___	_____	___
___	_____	___
___	_____	___
___	_____	___
___	_____	___

····································· ·····································
····································· ·····································
····································· ·····································
····································· ·····································
····································· ·····································
····································· ·····································
····································· ·····································
····································· ·····································
····································· ·····································
····································· ·····································

#	ACTIONS I WILL TAKE TO ACHIEVE MY GOAL	DATE COMPL'D
___	_____	___
___	_____	___
___	_____	___
___	_____	___
___	_____	___
___	_____	___
___	_____	___
___	_____	___
___	_____	___
___	_____	___

GOAL 1 NOTES

30/100 PERCENT

....
....
....
....
....
....
....
....
....
....

#	MORE ACTIONS I WILL TAKE TO ACHIEVE MY GOAL	DATE COMPL'D

MONTH 3: WEEK 1

30/100 PERCENT

MONTH, DAY - YEAR

MONDAY

....
....
....

%

TUESDAY

....
....

....

WEDNESDAY

....
....

....

THURSDAY

....
....

....

WRITE A SHORT THREE LINE SYNOPSIS (ABOUT THE SAME AMOUNT AS YOU WOULD TWITTER) FOR EACH DAY AND RECORD YOUR PERCENTAGE

FRIDAY

....
....

....

SATURDAY

....
....

....

SUNDAY

....
....
....

....

SUB-TOTAL _____

DIVIDED BY 7

÷ 7 =

THIS WEEK'S AVERAGE _____

How do you feel about week 9?

....
....
....
....
....

What could you have done differently?

....
....
....
....
....

What will you do differently next week?

....
....
....
....
....

Are you adding anything to week 10?   ___Yes   ___No
If yes, What?

....
....
....

If no, Why Not?

....
....
....

Other enlightening notes, thoughts
or observations about this week.
What worked and Why?
What didn't and Why Not?

_____

_____

_____

_____

_____

_____

_____

_____

MATTHEW 17:19 - 20

If you have faith as small as a
mustard seed, you can say to this
mountain, 'Move from here
to there' and it will move.
Nothing will be impossible
for you.

FAITH

MONTH 3: WEEK 2

30 / **100**
PERCENT

%

MONTH, DAY - YEAR

MONDAY

....
....
....

....

TUESDAY

....
....

....

WEDNESDAY

....
....

....

THURSDAY

....
....

....

FRIDAY

....
....

....

SATURDAY

....
....

....

SUNDAY

....
....
....

....

WRITE
A
SHORT
THREE LINE
SYNOPSIS
(ABOUT THE
SAME AMOUNT
AS YOU WOULD
TWITTER)
FOR
EACH
DAY
AND
RECORD
YOUR
PERCENTAGE

SUB-TOTAL   _____

DIVIDED BY 7   ÷ **7** =

THIS WEEK'S AVERAGE   _____

How do you feel about week 10?

....
....
....
....
....

What could you have done differently?

....
....
....
....
....

What will you do differently next week?

....
....
....
....
....

Are you adding anything to week 11?   ___Yes   ___No
If yes, What?

....
....
....

If no, Why Not?

....
....
....

Other enlightening notes, thoughts
or observations about this week.
What worked and Why?
What didn't and Why Not?

_____

_____

_____

_____

_____

_____

_____

_____

"Chance allows you to
accomplish a goal every
once in a while,
but consistent achievement
happens only if you love
what you are doing."
— Bart Conner

PASSION

MONTH 3: WEEK 3

MONTH, DAY - YEAR

MONDAY

....

....

....

TUESDAY

....

....

....

WEDNESDAY

....

....

....

THURSDAY

....

....

....

FRIDAY

....

....

....

SATURDAY

....

....

....

SUNDAY

....

....

....

%

WRITE
A
SHORT
THREE LINE
SYNOPSIS
*(ABOUT THE
SAME AMOUNT
AS YOU WOULD
TWITTER)*
FOR
EACH
DAY
AND
RECORD
YOUR
PERCENTAGE

SUB-TOTAL _____

DIVIDED BY 7   ÷ **7** =

THIS WEEK'S AVERAGE _____

DO NOT FEEL COMPELLED TO ADD ANYTHING NEW UNTIL YOU HAVE MASTERED
THE THING YOU ARE DETERMINED TO ACCOMPLISH!

How do you feel about week 11?

....
....
....
....
....

What could you have done differently?

....
....
....
....
....

What will you do differently next week?

....
....
....
....
....

Are you adding anything to week 12?   ___Yes   ___No
If yes, What?

....
....
....

If no, Why Not?

....
....
....

Other enlightening notes, thoughts
or observations about this week.
What worked and Why?
What didn't and Why Not?

_____
_____
_____
_____
_____
_____
_____
_____
_____
_____

HEBREWS 11:1

Faith is the substance
of things hoped for,
the evidence of
things unseen.

**CONFIDENT
EXPECTATION**

MONTH 3: WEEK 4

MONTH, DAY   -   YEAR

%

MONDAY

....
....
....

TUESDAY

....
....
....

WEDNESDAY

....
....
....

THURSDAY

....
....
....

FRIDAY

....
....
....

SATURDAY

....
....
....

SUNDAY

....
....
....

WRITE
A
SHORT
THREE LINE
SYNOPSIS
*(ABOUT THE
SAME AMOUNT
AS YOU WOULD
TWITTER)*
FOR
EACH
DAY
AND
RECORD
YOUR
PERCENTAGE

SUB-TOTAL   _____

DIVIDED BY 7   ÷ **7** =

THIS WEEK'S AVERAGE   _____

DO NOT FEEL COMPELLED TO ADD ANYTHING NEW UNTIL YOU HAVE MASTERED
THE THING YOU ARE DETERMINED TO ACCOMPLISH!

How do you feel about week 12?

....
....
....
....

What could you have done differently?

....
....
....
....
....

What will you do differently next week?

....
....
....
....
....

Are You Adding **ANOTHER 30 DAYS**?   __Yes   __No
If yes, Why have you decided to?

....
....
....

If no, Why Not?

....
....
....

Other enlightening notes, thoughts
or observations about this week.
What worked and Why?
What didn't and Why Not?

_____

_____

_____

_____

_____

_____

_____

_____

_____

_____

"Winners compare their
achievements with their goals,
while losers compare their
achievements with those of
other people."

—Nido Qubein

SELF ASSESSMENT

MONTH 3: EXTRA DAYS

MONTH, DAY - YEAR

MONDAY

....
....

.... **%**

TUESDAY

....
....

....

WEDNESDAY

....
....

....

THURSDAY

....
....

....

FRIDAY

....
....

....

SATURDAY

....
....

....

SUNDAY

....
....
....

....

WRITE A SHORT THREE LINE SYNOPSIS *(ABOUT THE SAME AMOUNT AS YOU WOULD TWITTER,* FOR EACH DAY AND RECORD YOUR PERCENTAGE

SUB-TOTAL _____

DIVIDED BY 7   ÷ **7** =

THIS WEEK'S AVERAGE _____

NOTES

·······························
·······························
·······························
·······························
·······························
·······························
·······························
·······························
·······························
·······························
·······························
·······························
·······························
·······························
·······························
·······························
·······························
·······························
·······························
·······························

> "Happiness does not come from doing easy work but from the afterglow of satisfaction that comes after the achievement of a difficult task that demanded our best."
>
> —Theodore Isaac Rubin
>
> **100 PERCENT**

MONTH 3 _____

30/100 PERCENT

WEEK 1

....
....
....
....

WEEK 2

....
....
....
....

WEEK 3

....
....
....
....

WEEK 4

....
....
....
....

EXTRA DAYS

....
....
....

WRITE
A
SHORT
THREE LINE
SYNOPSIS
*(ABOUT THE
SAME AMOUNT
AS YOU WOULD
TWITTER,*
FOR
EACH
DAY
AND
RECORD
YOUR
PERCENTAGE

SUB-TOTAL   _____

DIVIDED BY 4   ÷ **4** =

THIS MONTHS AVERAGE   _____

NOTES

....

....

....

....

....

....

....

....

....

....

....

....

....

....

....

....

....

....

....

....

Other enlightening notes, thoughts
or observations about this week.
What worked and Why?
What didn't and Why Not?

_____

_____

_____

_____

_____

_____

_____

_____

_____

2 TIMOTHY 1:17

God did not give you a spirit
of timidity, but a spirit of
Power, of Love and of
Self-Discipline.

FEARLESSNESS

MONTH 3 MY TRIUMPHS

....
....
....
....
....
....
....
....
....
....
....
....
....
....

> "When you do nothing,
> you feel overwhelmed and powerless.
> But when you get involved,
> you feel the sense of hope
> and accomplishment that comes
> from knowing you are
> working to make things better."
>
> **NOW**

MAINTENANCE

In the end, maintenance speaks directly to your commitment to preserve and grow the new you at 100%. It's the new you, whether you just created it, or you just found it again.

Think about the people that you know who live life at 100%. Kobe Bryant does it for the Lakers. Lebron James does it for the Cleveland Cavaliers. David Beckham does it for AC Milan, and Tiger Woods just does it. When Andre Agassi stopped doing it for the fans he kept doing it for his foundation that is dedicated helping kids by transforming U.S. public education for underserved youth. When Magic Johnson stopped doing it for the Lakers, he reinvented himself as a businessman, and started doing it for his community by getting companies to invest in underserved urban communities.

You can do it, too. After three months of 30 DAYS AT 100 PERCENT, you can decide to maintain the forward motion in your life by continuing to improve its quality, and by tackling one goal after another until you discover the purpose that God has for your life.

It was in the action that followed the decision to write *The Hair Makeup and Fashion Styling Career Guide* that I found out that I could—write. It was in the writing of an outline for a class and the delivery of it to three students who showed up for my first workshop that I found out that I could teach. And it was in the invitation to give the commencement address for Brooks College that I learned that I could write and deliver a keynote address. The purpose came after the action that accompanied the goal to create something. Now, I find that all I want to do is serve God by doing what I can to improve the lives of those around me.

Make a decision to take action, and make that decision every single day if you have to. You're human. So am I, and from time to time, we may fall off the wagon. So give yourself a break, let it go, then get back on the horse. Living life at 100% must become a lifestyle with a payoff that you are invested in.

I have maintained my weight within 5-6 pounds of my ideal 153 pounds for twenty-seven years because I made a **decision** and a **choice** to be the very best I could be, and that meant being 153 pounds where I am healthy, feel beautiful, and ready to take on the world. At 160 pounds I feel sluggish, none of my clothes fit, and I don't like visitors. The choice for me is simple. Not easy to maintain, but simple.

MAINTENANCE

Now it's your turn. Make a decision, choose a path and thrive—30 days at a time!

I set up an online community for 30 DAYS AT 100 PERCENT. What? You thought I was going to leave you out here all by yourself with no support? No way, I want to hear about all of your successes. I want to know what's working, what's not, and I want to be able to let you know when I do my first 30 DAYS AT 100 PERCENT workshop so that I can meet you.

Visit **30daysat100percent.ning.com** and set up yet another profile. Please write me: **crystal@30daysat100percent.com**.

....
....
....
....
....
....
....
....

....
....
....
....
....
....
....
....
....
....
....
....

> "The big secret in life,
> is that there is no big secret.
> Whatever your goal, you can get there if
> you're willing to work."
> —Oprah Winfrey
>
> **CONSISTENCY**

30/100 PERCENT

GOAL 2: _____

DATE CREATED: _____

DEFINE

GOAL ▸ _____
_____
_____
_____

PURPOSE ▸ _____
_____
_____
_____

PAYOFF ▸ _____
_____
_____
_____

#	ACTIONS I WILL TAKE TO ACHIEVE MY GOAL	DATE COMPL'D
___	_____	___
___	_____	___
___	_____	___
___	_____	___
___	_____	___
___	_____	___
___	_____	___
___	_____	___
___	_____	___
___	_____	___
___	_____	___

30/100 PERCENT

EXPAND THE VISION

ACHIEVE DATE: _____

◄ **WHO**
   will I be

◄ **WHAT**
   will I Gain

◄ **WHEN**
   will it Happen

◄ **WHY**
   is it Important

◄ **HOW**
   will I Benefit

#	MORE ACTIONS I WILL TAKE TO ACHIEVE MY GOAL	DATE COMPL'D

GOAL 2 NOTES

GOAL 2 NOTES

....

....

....

....

....

....

....

....

....

....

....

....

....

....

....

....

....

....

....

....

....

....

....

....

....

....

ISAIAH 30: 21

Whether you turn to the right or the left,
your ears will hear a voice behind you,
saying
"This is the way; walk in it"

DIRECTION

GOAL 3: _____

DEFINE

GOAL ▸ _____
_____
_____
_____

PURPOSE ▸ _____
_____
_____
_____

PAYOFF ▸ _____
_____
_____
_____

#	ACTIONS I WILL TAKE TO ACHIEVE MY GOAL	DATE COMPL'D
___	_____	_____
___	_____	_____
___	_____	_____
___	_____	_____
___	_____	_____
___	_____	_____
___	_____	_____
___	_____	_____
___	_____	_____
___	_____	_____
___	_____	_____

30/100 PERCENT

_____

EXPAND THE VISION   ACHIEVE DATE: _____

◀ **WHO**
will I be

◀ **WHAT**
will I Gain

◀ **WHEN**
will it Happen

◀ **WHY**
is it Important

◀ **HOW**
will I Benefit

#	MORE ACTIONS I WILL TAKE TO ACHIEVE MY GOAL	DATE COMPL'D
___	_____	_____
___	_____	_____
___	_____	_____
___	_____	_____
___	_____	_____
___	_____	_____
___	_____	_____
___	_____	_____
___	_____	_____
___	_____	_____

GOAL 3 NOTES

....
....
....
....
....
....
....
....
....
....
....
....
....
....
....
....
....
....

> "Change will not come if we wait for some other person or some other time. We are the ones we've been waiting for. We are the change that we seek."
>
> —President Barack Obama
>
> **YOU ARE THE ANSWER**

CWL – Speaking
AREA/CATEGORY/PROJECT

____ Write Mixxed In Speech 4 June 17
____ Review Audio for Pickups
____ Organize Audio

Personal
AREA/CATEGORY/PROJECT

____ P/U Tailored Shirts from Hans
____ Dry Cleaners
____ Read, Bible, Meditate
____ Monifa – Name for new Line
____ 1st4OLD Articles for Donna M.

CWL – Books
AREA/CATEGORY/PROJECT

____ Alcone (8)
____ Cosmix (13)
____ Reorder Calls
____ -Cinema   -Nigels
____ -Naimies   -Frends
____ Receivables
____ -Itomura
____ -Glammin
____ Content

CWL – Other
AREA/CATEGORY/PROJECT

____ Online Merchant Processing/BofA
____ -Return Policy
____ -Attorney letter
____ Uprinting – Brochure reprint
____ 30 days – "Purpose" Permission

AREA/CATEGORY/PROJECT

___ _____
___ _____
___ _____
___ _____
___ _____
___ _____
___ _____
___ _____

AREA/CATEGORY/PROJECT

___ _____
___ _____
___ _____
___ _____
___ _____
___ _____
___ _____
___ _____

AREA/CATEGORY/PROJECT

___ _____
___ _____
___ _____
___ _____
___ _____
___ _____
___ _____
___ _____

AREA/CATEGORY/PROJECT

___ _____
___ _____
___ _____
___ _____
___ _____
___ _____
___ _____
___ _____

30/100 PERCENT

CONFERENCE CALL _ WEEK_

NO CROSS TALK. NO FIXING OTHER PEOPLES' CHALLENGES. NO INTERRUPTIONS EXCEPT FOR A TIME STAMP. WHAT HAPPENS ON THE CALL STAYS ON THE CALL.

What's Working?

1) ....
....
....
....

2) ....
....
....
....

What's Not?

1) ....
....
....
....

2) ....
....
....
....

What successes have you had so far?

1) ....
....
....
....

2) ....
....
....
....

What challenges are you experiencing?

1) ....
....
....
....

2) ....
....
....
....

NOTES: ....
....
....
....
....

CONFERENCE CALL _ WEEK_

NO CROSS TALK. NO FIXING OTHER PEOPLES' CHALLENGES. NO INTERRUPTIONS EXCEPT FOR A TIME STAMP. WHAT HAPPENS ON THE CALL STAYS ON THE CALL.

What's Working?

1) ....

....

....

....

2) ....

....

....

....

What's Not?

1) ....

....

....

....

2) ....

....

....

....

What successes have you had so far?

1) ....

....

....

....

2) ....

....

....

....

What challenges are you experiencing?

1) ....

....

....

....

2) ....

....

....

....

NOTES: ....

....

....

....

....

ARE YOU READING?

1. Check out **The Purpose Driven Life: What on Earth Am I Here For?** by Rick Warren

2. Check out **Your Best Life Now: 7 Steps to Living at Your Full Potential** by Joel Osteen www.faithwords.com

3. Check out **Coach Wooden's Pyramid of Success: Building Blocks for a Better Life** by John Wooden & Jay Carty.

ARE YOU LISTENING?

1. Check out **Get The Edge** by Anthony Robbins.

ARE YOU WATCHING?

1. Check out **The Secret** Prime Time Productions. www.thesecret.tv.

ACKNOWLEDGEMENTS

FRIENDS SUPPORTERS & BENEFACTORS
KATHY BLOUNT
FLEACE´ WEAVER
MONIFA MORTIS
DARRELL JOHNSON
BINH KHUU & VANESSA DOAN

CONTENT & COPY EDITORS
MY SISTER GINA DUNCAN
JERRAM SWARTZ

AUDIO DIRECTOR
MICHAEL STRADFORD

AUDIO PRODUCER
SHAUN DREW
SOTTO VOCE PRODUCTIONS
818.694.3052

STUDIO & MASTERING
www.SOTTOVOCESTUDIO.com

THE CLINICAL TRIAL
JESSICA BURKS
ARVELLA "ALI BA BA" ROBERTS
STEPHANIE FLOR
GENEVIEVE SANTOS
FALLON SEABORN
QUIANA MCCANTS
KOBE & MEKHI LIPSEY

PHOTOGRAPHY
JSQUARED PHOTOGRAPHY
CANDACE CHERI AMOUR PRODUCTIONS